Diaries of War

Two Visual Accounts from Ukraine and Russia

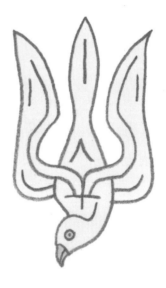

Nora Krug

PARTICULAR BOOKS
an imprint of
PENGUIN BOOKS

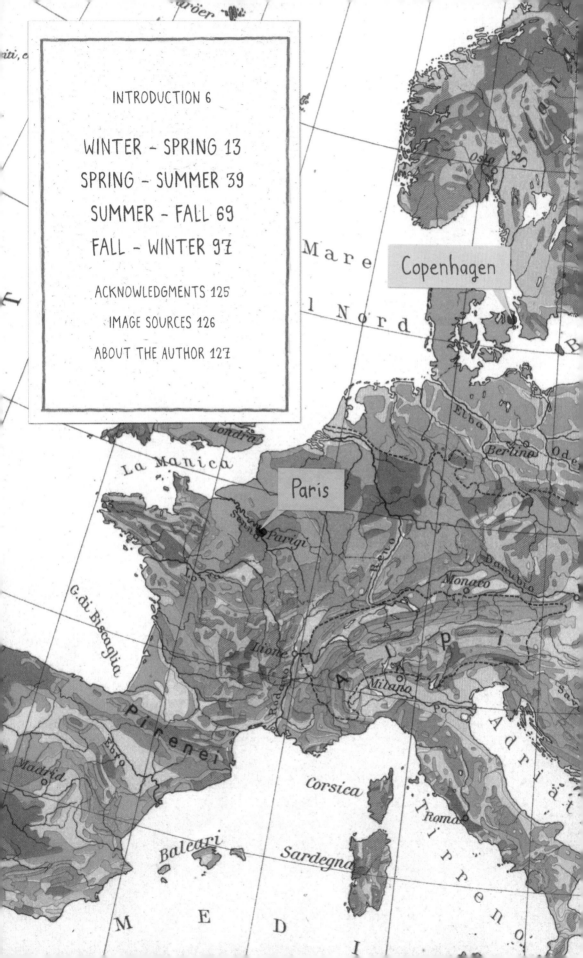

INTRODUCTION 6

WINTER – SPRING 13
SPRING – SUMMER 39
SUMMER – FALL 69
FALL – WINTER 97

ACKNOWLEDGMENTS 125
IMAGE SOURCES 126
ABOUT THE AUTHOR 127

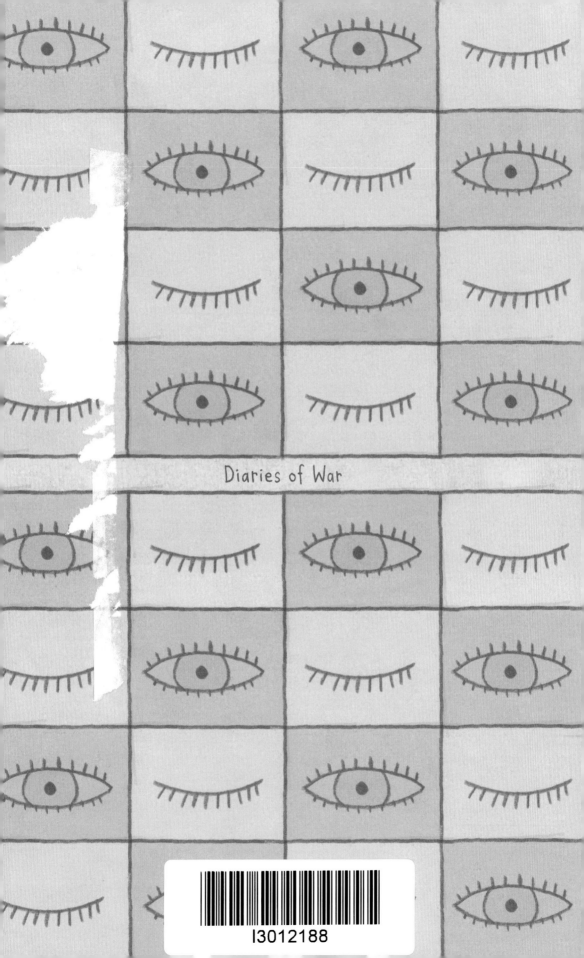

Diaries of War

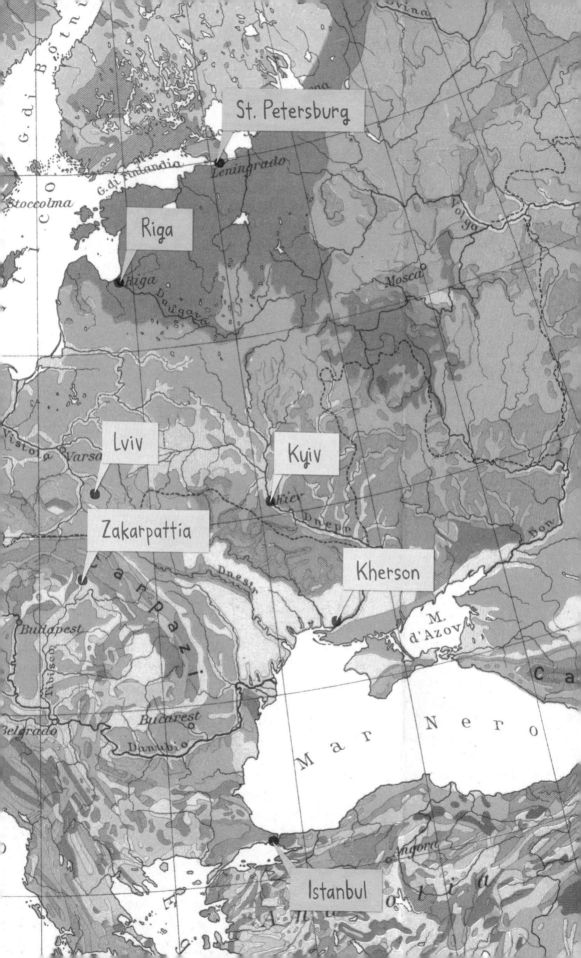

St. Petersburg

Riga

Lviv

Kyiv

Zakarpattia

Kherson

Istanbul

Introduction

On February 24, 2022, Russia launched a renewed and unprovoked full-scale military attack against Ukraine, aimed to stamp out the country, its culture, and its people.

As the events of this war unfolded over the next few days, I reached out to K., a journalist based in Kyiv, and D., an artist from St. Petersburg who opposes the war — both of whom I'd been in touch with only once online and had never met in person — to ask how they were. I was moved by the rawness of their responses, and I understood that, unlike most of what I had read about this war in the media, the personal accounts of these individuals might provide an emotional entry point to understanding the everyday reality of the war's devastating impact for those of us not immediately affected. I asked K. and D. if I could interview them about their experiences to create a weekly illustrated diary that would juxtapose their individual, contrasting voices and raise immediate awareness of the war. Both of them instantly agreed.

Over the course of the next twelve months, I communicated with them individually via text message. Every week, I asked how they were feeling, what they were thinking about and what they had experienced during the previous week. In addition to documenting their everyday experiences, I also posed questions that I hoped would shed light on how the war affected them on a deeper, more existential level: What impact did the war have on their minds and bodies? How did it change their relationship to their families and their sense of cultural belonging? Did it make them think differently about guilt, sacrifice, reparation and retribution? Why do we wage wars, and will we ever learn from them?

Throughout the year, I became better acquainted with K. and D., previously strangers to me, asking them such personal questions that I would normally only ask of my closest friends. In real time, I shaped their individual accounts and responses into a consistent narrative, changed certain details to maintain their anonymity, passed the text by them for final approval and then created the accompanying illustrations based on my research and my imagination.

A portion of the diary entries was serialized in the *Los Angeles Times* between February 2022 and February 2023. Excerpts also appeared in *L'Espresso* (Italy), *El País* (Spain), *Süddeutsche Zeitung* (Germany) and *De Volkskrant* (Holland). Each week's entry was created in real time.

———

Ukraine has a long, rich and complicated history. Like that of many other European countries, it is a history of cultural achievements, wars and moving borders. Over the centuries, present-day Ukrainian territories were ruled, suppressed and colonized by various external states, federations, khanates and empires. The 20th century marked a new period of upheaval: Ukraine fought for independence when the Russian Empire was overthrown in 1917; incurred forced Russian cultural assimilation and a period of starvation brought on by Stalin's policies in the 1930s; suffered under the occupation of the Axis powers during WWII; experienced further periods of Russification; and declared independence again in 1991, when the Soviet Union collapsed.

After the disintegration of the USSR, Ukraine gave up its nuclear arsenal in exchange for being guaranteed sovereignty as a country by the other signatories of the disarmament contract — including Russia. Despite political and economic reforms, Ukraine struggled with instability and corruption and faced repeated attempts by Russia of exerting control over the country. Pro-democracy protests ensued in 2004, and when a Ukrainian president chose to abandon a free-trade agreement with the European Union in favor of prioritizing closer ties to Russia in 2013, violent demonstrations erupted, which led to what came to be known as the Revolution of Dignity, a movement whose intent was to establish democratic values.

Soon after, Russia annexed Crimea, a peninsula in the Black Sea that had been contested over the centuries by various peoples, states, khanates, countries and empires, and that had been under Soviet Ukrainian authority since 1954 and under full legal Ukrainian jurisdiction since 1995. A war broke out in Eastern Ukraine, in the Donbas region, with the Ukrainian army and pro-Ukrainian battalions on one side, and armed Russian-backed Ukrainian separatists and Russian troops on the other. While the deadly war in the Donbas continued, Russia repeatedly struck Ukraine with a series of cyberattacks that affected its key infrastructure.

In 2022, Russia's president Vladimir Putin launched a renewed, full-on attack on Ukraine under the pretext of "reuniting" Ukrainians and Russians as one homogenous people, stopping a "genocide" against Russian-speaking residents in the Donbas and eradicating "Nazism" in Ukraine, a country whose historical formation, sovereignty and distinct cultural identity he questions. By doing so, he ignores history and international law and hides Russia's real intentions: to colonize and destroy Ukraine and its culture in order to strengthen its own totalitarian and extremist political position and sphere of influence. Russia's recent invasion has been denounced by the United Nations and by democracies around the world.

———

D.'s and K.'s identities are as complex as Ukraine's history. Their perspectives are shaped by their individual family histories, their professional environments and the distinct cultural experiences and political realities in which they have found themselves. D. has German and Russian-Jewish ancestry, but he feels no cultural connection to Germany or to Judaism. He was born in a small town in Soviet Russia and moved to St. Petersburg when he was twenty years old. He returns to his hometown only to visit his mother. When people from abroad ask him where he is from, he tells them St. Petersburg instead of Russia, because he identifies more strongly with his city than with his country.

K. was born in the Volga region, in the western part of Russia, during the days of the Soviet Union. She has Inuit, Jewish and Cossack ancestry, and as a child, her grandfather told her stories about his Cossack village and sang Ukrainian folksongs to her. At the young age of thirteen, she relocated to Crimea, Ukraine, with her mother and spent the formative years of her youth there. After graduating from high school, K. returned to Russia to study journalism and begin her career as a reporter. As the editor-in-chief of a regional Russian newspaper that openly declared its opposition to Vladimir Putin's regime, she refused to cooperate with the Russian Federal Security Service, which resulted in the newspaper being raided and shut down. Soon after, K. moved back to Ukraine to continue her work as a journalist. When the war in the Donbas began, K. reported on it from both sides of the frontline and for both Ukrainian and anti-Kremlin Russian news outlets. In 2015, she traded her Russian passport for a Ukrainian one, which she was given in part for her reporting on the war in the Donbas. K. no longer culturally identifies with contemporary Russia. Since Russia's recent invasion, she has been reporting from the frontline of the war, risking her life daily to defend Ukraine's freedom and values. As a Russia-born Ukrainian, her perspective is not unique, but it is more complex than that of many other journalists.

———

How can the voices of two individuals with such complicated and contrasting identities contribute to our understanding of the current war in Ukraine? Individual narratives are often overlooked in the writing of history, and yet they allow us a different kind of entry point, a nuanced and emotional understanding of what most historians, journalists and writers seek: the truth. Facts are important and incontestable, while individual experiences can never be entirely objective, nor do they present a complete picture of the political situations that they grow out of. But personal narratives shed light on different aspects of the truth and are therefore important components of it.

Despite their differences, D. and K. are both witnesses. In order to understand the human cost of this war, it was important to record those personal voices, these distilled moments in time, immediately as the political events unfolded. *Diaries of War* does not aim to substantiate a particular, pre-existing narrative, to portray a quintessential Russian or Ukrainian perspective or to represent a definite guide to understanding Russia's criminal war on Ukraine. My objective is not to create a space for reconciliation, to equalize the Russian and Ukrainian experiences, to victimize the Russian side or to tell the story of a "good Russian." Rather, the project's goal is to document the stark contrast between two narratives shaped by this war on opposite sides of the border and to highlight D.'s and K.'s multifaceted identities and experiences by placing them in direct proximity to each other on the page.

Both D. and K. were born in the Soviet Union but have spent many years of their lives in two very different societies whose distinct cultures have shaped the way they think. D. speaks openly about his anti-Putin views in his diary entries, and allowing himself to be interviewed about his views involves a certain risk. At the same time, he admits that he is too afraid to voice his views in public. He can only trust people he knows and with whom he shares the same opinions. Not being able to speak to others about his thoughts and feelings makes him feel afraid and isolated. In contrast, as a journalist, taking a public position on the war, and talking and writing about it, is K.'s main activity and responsibility. Through her work, she connects with her friends and peers, and with the Ukrainians she interviews and writes about. In stark contrast to D., speaking her mind is K.'s strategy for survival. Both K. and D. find themselves in unfamiliar situations, isolated from their families, but they experience the war in vastly different ways: K. lives in constant fear of her home being bombed; of her friends and colleagues being kidnapped, tortured or killed; of her Ukrainian family being harmed. D.'s struggle is more passive and internal: The war has estranged him from his country and makes him feel emotionally paralyzed. Although he contributes money to Ukrainian causes, he admits to his fear of taking part in public demonstrations and to the fact that he is not an activist. K. has clear goals: for Ukraine to win the war, and for her family to be reunited. D. wishes for his family to be reunited as well, but he has no clear idea of what his future should be, where he should live or whether and how his country will evolve into a democracy.

———

When I first conceived of this project, I was uncertain as to whether showing a Russian perspective was justified. For decades, the world has tolerated and thus indirectly sustained Russia's revisionist narratives, expansionist policies and genocidal tactics while undermining Ukraine's self-determination. As a European, I understand that the war in Ukraine is about the future of all of Europe, and that Ukrainians are paying the deadly toll for our freedom. As a German, I believe that we have to correct our mistakes of the past. Democracy is just a utopian concept if it doesn't include our neighbors, and *pacifism* remains an empty word if we cannot provide active military, financial and ideological support to democracies who are attacked by tyrannical regimes. At the same time, I am aware that I am coming at the project as an outsider. K.'s and D.'s perspectives are utterly different from my Western European point of view because I do not share their individual stories or their distinct histories. As an outsider, I will never be able to fully grasp the extent of the Ukrainian suffering.

But contemporary Russia's politics of colonial aggression feel uncomfortably familiar. As the granddaughter of a "follower," a German who neither actively supported nor resisted the Nazi regime, I understand the importance of highlighting ambiguous, complex and sometimes contradictory narratives — narratives that are perhaps difficult to accept — because they are often overlooked despite the fact that they are necessary to our understanding of how dictatorships take form and are sustained. It is easy to celebrate a hero or to condemn a perpetrator. But it is ambivalent narratives that force us to critically confront our own passivity, to challenge the fallibility of our own moral integrity.

As a visual journalist, my responsibility is to the truth, and to accurately and sensitively document the perspectives of my two protagonists, even when I didn't agree with them. I strongly believe that we can influence and change our governments, and I believe that it is our responsibility to actively resist injustice. To those of us living far away and watching from the sidelines, simply telling ourselves that we do not know how we would act, what we would do in the face of a tyrannical regime is not enough. Admitting to our fear of taking action should merely be the starting point for a deeper inner confrontation. A war can never be blamed solely on a single despotic leader and his propaganda. When thinking about the Third Reich, we often forget that people actually had a choice: between remaining passive or resisting in big or in small but significant ways. We also have a choice today. And what we decide to do or not to do will have direct consequences for the lives of others. What would the world look like today without those who resisted tyrannical regimes in the past? What will it look like tomorrow?

Кіевъ.   Большая Владимірская улица.

Winter – Spring

The first thing I did after I found out that war came to Kyiv was take a bath. I sat there for half an hour. I can't describe how I feel. But I know that this is the end of Putin's Russia.

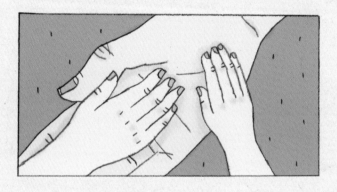

We are still in Kyiv with the kids. They are two and six. It is not easy to be with them and keep calm. It's scary. But Ukraine is very strong, and its people are awesome.

We arrived safely in Lviv. We now live in the neighborhood that used to be the ghetto back in 1941. In front of my window there is a railway. Every thirty minutes I see trains with civilians going west, and trains with tanks going east. Eighty years ago, this railway served the Nazis: Their trains took Jews to concentration camps, and soon after, those same trains took people from Lviv to the gulags, as many were accused of being collaborators.

Terrible. Worst days of my life. Putin kills my country.
I'm afraid that a lot of people are still with him. I am drinking
wine with my wife and we are discussing the idea of emigrating.

I'm okay. I'm just trying to figure out a way to emigrate.
We have two kids, nine and ten, and a dog. I am the
only one with a passport and a visa.

I'm in contact with a Russian friend in Ukraine,
to try to help her with information.

I'm a bit speechless these days.
It's day 12, and this nightmare still continues.

We help journalists with equipment, vests and helmets so they can report safely. Today was one of those rare days we didn't hear sirens. This is what I call "happy hours."

Last night I went to the Lviv railway station where I had to meet a family who brought our children's clothes from Kyiv. There were thousands of people trying to figure out where to go. Many people warmed themselves near barrels of fire. I felt absolutely useless and powerless.

I'd say I'm OK. Just working on a way to emigrate, and to pursue my work outside of Russia. Facebook is officially blocked in Russia. I can still use it here with VPN.

PUTIN-KHUYLO! ("Khuylo" is Russian for "dick.")
It's midnight here, so I'll try to sleep.

Every day when I wake up, I feel pain in my stomach. It's a mix of fear, anger and hatred. How many innocent people have died during the night? How many will die today?

I don't want to leave Ukraine. I want to send my kids abroad. My plan is to take them to Denmark where my mother recently evacuated to and then come back to work.

I hardly slept last night. The sirens started at 2:30 AM, and then I was lying there listening to the explosions. The kids are fine. They don't hear anything at night.

I need to have some rest. It was a day full of terrible events: colleagues killed, interviews with people who escaped from hell.

I'm still in stress, but not in panic like I was during the first days.

We started talking to the children about the war on the second day. We just told them what's going on. They faced the consequences a few days ago — they had saved money and wanted to buy a new Nintendo game but it didn't work out because Nintendo shut down in Russia.

The last time I demonstrated was after Alexey Navalny's arrest. Every time I felt some euphoria when I saw a lot of people who disagree with Putin's regime. But at the same time, I realized that even more people support him.

I told my six-year-old boy that it's war. He cried because he misses his pal from preschool who is now in Lithuania. They call each other every day to discuss Minecraft.

I'm in transit to Warsaw with the kids.
So many loud sounds, like fireworks.
So many Ukrainians on the streets.

We've arrived in Copenhagen and it's so silent here. Only the airplanes disturb me because they sound threatening. We have thousands of books here, and a garden with singing birds and sunshine. It's a great relief for me that my kids are in a safe place.

But I can't sit here while my country is on fire and my husband is there, unable to get out.

I know people who are pro-Putin, but not in my social circle. One more reason to emigrate is this poster that I've seen in public spaces: "We don't abandon our own."

It's impossible to breathe freely here. You live with the fear that they might come for you. I really don't want my kids to grow up in this atmosphere. I was a teenager in the '90s, after the Soviet Union had collapsed. That's when I fell in love with freedom.

I'll emigrate alone. I'll go and organize everything, then my family will join me. My friends in Riga found a place where I can stay for free for four months. I'm really nervous and afraid. What if my family can't come? What if I can't make money there? But at the same time I understand that I need fresh air, that I can't find it in Russia. What if there's no fresh air there either?

It's sunny here, and it feels like spring is coming. At first, the boys were frustrated because of the relocation. The younger one didn't smile and refused to eat. The older one got more Lego sets — Minecraft and Harry Potter — which made him absolutely happy.

I spend my days speaking with Mariupol survivors and interviewing people in the occupied territories. I don't feel like I've actually left Ukraine. I thought I heard a siren in the middle of the night, and my husband's voice announcing: "Attention, air raid alert, everyone get down to the bomb shelter!" He spends his nights on the floor of the bathroom because there are no windows.

Yesterday my older boy put a teapot cover on his head which made him look like a wizard, and he asked us to make a wish. I wished that the war would end. He replied: "Your wish will be fulfilled in the next few days, I promise."

I don't have a TV. I don't want to watch propaganda.
I get most of my news on the Russian Kremlin-critical platforms
Meduza.io and Novaya Gazeta. My wife and I just watched an
interview with Volodymyr Zelensky. He is amazing.

I try not to speak about the war with people who aren't my
friends. I'm afraid that somebody might tell the police about
my opinions. I'm not an activist, but on the first day of the war,
I signed a petition and told everyone that I'm against it. I imagined
that the police would come to my studio, but they didn't.

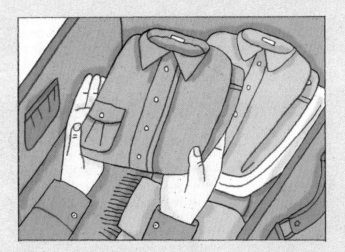

I was planning to go to Helsinki tomorrow by train, but the
last train will be leaving today. The Finnish train company has
closed down all its trains in Russia. So I bought a bus ticket.
My friends from Finland sent me a work contract so I can cross
the Russian border. There is a possibility that I can't get out,
so we decided not to tell the kids yet that I am emigrating.
They are on vacation at their grandma's now.

I'll go back to Ukraine on Tuesday! My colleagues and I are organizing an emergency medicine training event for journalists in Kyiv. I haven't told the kids yet that I'm leaving. They should be okay staying with my mom in Denmark. I want to see my home in Kyiv so much. I miss my turntable, my books and my friends. I don't know if my house was hit. I imagine everything looking the same way as before, as if the war had never happened.

Last night, I heard a female voice from somewhere down below in the basement, begging for help. I was sure I heard it, but I checked the whole house, and I couldn't find anyone. I think it was a hallucination.

I saw the photos of the massacres in Bucha and Irpin. The only thought I have in my mind is that I don't know how to live in a world where something like this happens.

Today the body of my colleague Max Levin was found near Kyiv. After he disappeared, I hoped he was still alive, possibly in Russian captivity. He was shot dead on March 13. He was a father of four sons and was my friend's husband.

Today I took a bus to Helsinki. We stayed at the Russian border for more than two hours because there were several Ukrainians on the bus. At the Finnish border, I helped a Ukrainian woman with a child by translating for her. She had problems with her documents but was finally allowed to enter. But the Finnish border guards didn't let me in. Not enough grounds to enter for work, they said, and my Sputnik vaccine doesn't work in the EU. So, I came back. I visited Finland just to smoke a cigarette.

I read an article in the Russian media justifying the "denazification" of Ukraine. I can't believe anyone could write this shit. Russians will have to face their guilt.

I'm thinking about other places to go. Estonia, or Turkey. My mother lives in a small town near St. Petersburg. She understands everything about the Putin regime. But she was upset when I told her about my plans to emigrate. She is afraid of being alone.

For Ukrainians, every day is associated with a number. Today it's forty-five. For forty-five days, Russia has been destroying everything we love.

I've arrived safely back in Lviv. We delivered about thirty protection kits to journalists. Not many things have made me feel good since the beginning of the Russian invasion, but journalists wearing vests and helmets is one such thing.

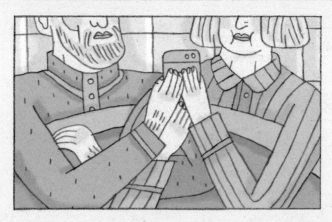

My husband's parents decided to stay in Kyiv. They are originally from Donetsk and had to flee when the war started there in 2014. They don't want to flee again. Some weeks ago, my father-in-law lost his memory for a few hours. At first, we thought it was a stroke, but the doctors couldn't find anything. I suspect this happened because that night a rocket was fired over their house. He couldn't even remember that there was a war. The doctors said he shouldn't spend so much time reading the news. Looking at photographs of our kids allows my parents-in-law to get through this hell. My sons have become children of war. Their generation is broken.

A few days after the war began, the government displayed a Russian flag near my house. It rained, and after a week or two, the flag looked like a cleaning rag. Last week it disappeared entirely, and only the flagpole was left. It looked to me like a symbol for what is currently happening with Russia.

I'm thinking more and more about parallels between Nazi Germany and today's Russia. A Russian literary critic wrote that "to be against the war is to be for Russia." I agree with her.

I've always been interested in Ukraine as a country. I've been to Kiev three times in my life. I felt depressed after Crimea's annexation. I would really like to visit Crimea, but as a Russian, I feel I have no right to go there.

A colleague of mine, who is also an artist, supports the war. It makes me sad. How is it possible that an artist who draws pictures about the siege of Leningrad can support this war?

We're back in Kyiv. My husband's parents cried when we arrived. My mother-in-law cooked pelmeni. Kyiv looks so dark and empty. My apartment is untouched. It's cold because there is no heating, but that's all right. I took my first bath since February 24. I never thought I would dream about taking a bath!

I went to Katyuzhanka near Kyiv, to film villagers who survived the Russian occupation. I saw destroyed Russian tanks and people standing in line for bread and potatoes. Seeing all the damage inflicted makes me think that most Russians support the invasion and don't understand anything about Ukrainians.

Yesterday I video-called my older son from our apartment. When he saw his room, he started to cry. He misses Kyiv very much. I told him that he can't return to Kyiv because there is nothing here for him: no kids, no preschool, and it's still very dangerous. I told him that I'll return to Denmark in two weeks but I'm not sure I will. I need to be here to report. I am tired, but somebody must replace my colleagues in the field.

Yesterday I walked by a school that had a sign with a Z displayed in its window. It's terrible. If this happens at my kids' school, I will speak out against it. I heard about other schools where such signs were removed because parents spoke out.

My guess is that 30% of Russians support the regime, 30% are against it and another 40% simply don't care because they are OK economically. I often think about what Russians can do to resist the regime, but I don't have an answer. Putin's death could bring about change. But I'd prefer seeing him in The Hague.

I cannot live here with Putin, his government and his police. I had planned to emigrate next week, but my kid's birthday is that week, so I think I'll leave right after. Still, I think about how much I belong in St. Petersburg, because it is my city. I moved here when I was twenty. It was here that I understood what I want to do with my life, and that I was able to create my art. I like walking around the city, cycling on the Fontanka River, suffering through the dark winters and enjoying the white summer nights, which often prevent me from sleeping. How can I leave my city?

I returned to Lviv, and I spoke to a woman who lost her son in Hostomel. The Russians executed him for no particular reason. He was helping locals escape the city when they captured him along with four other men and shot at him eight times. Her other son was injured during a shelling in Bucha. He's in hospital now and deeply depressed. She doesn't know how to continue living after all this happened.

I'm feeling very tired and anxious. According to my app, I spend ten hours a day looking at my phone. So many people have gone crazy because of the war. The hatred toward the Russians has turned into hatred toward ourselves. There are fights between those who have stayed in Ukraine and those who have now returned from the European Union, who are being accused of being weak. Sometimes I myself feel so angry, and don't know what to do with these feelings.

My older son starts school in Copenhagen on Monday. My mother, who is in Denmark, gave him a present: a backpack and a pencil case. He was so happy. He can't wait for his first lesson.

I saw my first dandelion. Usually, spring motivates me, but not this year. I read reports from Bucha, listen to military experts, look at photos of the war all day. It's very hard. I hope that the Russian army will lose the war. At the same time, I don't want those ordinary soldiers to die. I find myself wishing that Putin will die.

This feels bad because I never used to wish death on anyone. Now I feel such a desire. There is a cognitive dissonance in my head.

The government is preparing St. Petersburg for May 9, Victory Day. I can't understand how Russians can celebrate this day, given that we are the aggressors in this war.

I went to Moscow to meet with some artist friends. A lot of them are thinking of emigrating. One of my friends went to several rallies in Moscow. One time she was arrested by the police, then there was a humiliating trial and she was fined 30,000 rubles. Her friends raised the money for her. It seems to me that I live in some kind of bubble. Almost no one around me is in favor of the war. People in this country have been living in two different realities for a long time.

My older son went to school for the first time in his life last Monday, and I wasn't there to experience it with him. I'm on the bus on my way from Lviv to Warsaw. From there, I'll go to Copenhagen. I miss my kids. Playing with them, sleeping next to them, taking them to the zoo.

I'm not religious, but at Easter we normally gather with the family. We eat cakes and celebrate life. This year, we celebrated separately: my husband and I in Lviv, his parents in Kyiv, his grandparents in Sumy, and my kids and my mother in Copenhagen, 1,500 kilometers away from us. I used to find these gatherings boring. Now I miss them so much.

Like a carrier pigeon, constantly moving from one location to another, I'm transporting belongings and messages back and forth. Before the war, I used to film birds in our neighborhood in Kyiv. It felt therapeutic: watching those birds, their calmness. There is something magical about it. There is a war, everything around you is exploding, people are dying, but you are just a bird, living in your habitat, just a creature whose life remains the same.

We celebrated my kid's eleventh birthday yesterday. Now I'm in the car in Latvia with a friend. We'll arrive in Riga in two hours. I'm tired. We crossed the border without a problem because Estonia accepts the Russian Sputnik COVID vaccine.

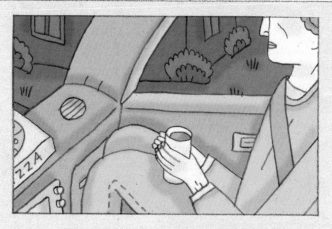

At the Russian border I saw buses filled with Ukrainians who had to wait for more than three hours.

I told my children that I'm going to Latvia for work, but I'll also look for ways to relocate here. I had some of my artwork shipped to Latvia, and I'll try to sell it from here. I would like to donate some of the money from my art sales to Ukraine. I am not an activist, but I think about how I can help Ukrainian people all the time. Last year, I received an art grant from the Norwegian government. The foundation tried to send me the money at the end of February, but it didn't go through. I asked them to donate the money to a Ukrainian humanitarian organization instead, and they did.

I'm so tired that it's hard for me to communicate.

When I'm in Denmark, like now, I miss my husband and my family in Ukraine. When I'm in Ukraine, I miss my kids. The saddest thing is that I can't put these two lives together, that I can't be in two places at the same time. If the war lasts months or years, what kind of life will we have?

I'm worried about my husband and the other men on my reporting team. When we gathered a few days ago in Lviv they were making jokes, saying that if they were drafted into the army, rather than working as journalists, at least they'd have helmets and vests to protect themselves. I don't want them to die.

I could never have imagined someone wanting to kill civilians, to bomb kids. But that's Russia's daily mission. We have no option but to win the war. If you give Russia something it wants, it will take more. Ukraine must win. For Ukrainians to think that Russia will change if Putin dies is stupid. Russia will be Ukraine's neighbor forever, whether we like it or not. And that scares me very much.

Here in Riga, I'm staying at the apartment of my friend's mother, a nice place with a kitchen where I can cook, a bathroom, a cat, a patio and flowers. I feel very strange. While I was still in Russia, I was sure that once I left everything would be easy. But it isn't. It's hard to read the news, and not be with my family. Yesterday I went to Tallinn, Estonia, to visit a friend who immigrated there two and a half years ago. We went to a concert of the Ukrainian singer Ivan Dorn, who is also very famous in Russia. He showed video footage from the war, and right from the start of the concert, I found myself ready to cry.

A few days ago, all public transportation was free because Latvia was celebrating their Declaration of Independence Day, which commemorates Latvia's independence from the USSR in 1990. I was born in the Soviet Union, but Russia is my home now, so I feel no personal connection.

Russia celebrated Victory Day this week. The days leading up to it are always scary; military planes fly over the cities and it is very noisy. The government has changed the meaning of this holiday to use it for the purpose of the current war.

Last Thursday I spent a day in my older son's school in Copenhagen. During breaktime, another Ukrainian student played a song by the Ukrainian rap band Kalush, which won this year's Eurovision song contest. Everybody in the classroom was dancing, including my son. They were so happy!

I'm thinking about dead bodies. When I started reporting from the war in the Donbas region in 2014, one of my colleagues told me to "follow the bodies." I didn't understand what he meant. He was documenting how Russians were returning the bodies of their dead soldiers from Donetsk to Russia. I've seen hundreds of dead Russian bodies stored in refrigerated vans across Ukraine, and nobody wants to take them back to Russia for burial. It says a lot about Russia's war against Ukraine. Russians don't even care about their own people. They use them as fodder for their God of War.

I've been in Riga for two weeks now, and I'm starting to get used to it. I miss my family but we talk on the phone almost every day. My children are asking when their dad will come home. I'll probably go back to St. Petersburg in the next few weeks to get some of the papers I need in order to emigrate.

My next-door neighbor in Riga told me that many Russian-speaking people in Latvia support Putin. I wonder why they live here, and not in Russia. On Victory Day, I saw a lot of people carrying flowers in Riga. They went to Victory Park to visit the Soviet Victory Monument. There were a lot of police, and the area directly around the monument was fenced off. The flowers were handed out to volunteers who laid them down in front of the monument. The next day I read online that the flowers had been removed by the city's sanitation services, because, allegedly, they froze overnight. Some people brought new flowers.
The last time I laid down flowers on Victory Day was as a pupil.

Spring — Summer

My son turned seven in Copenhagen, and I invited a close friend and her son to celebrate with us. It felt surreal, as if we had gone back to a time before the war.

My Russian acquaintances and distant relatives are all against Putin and Russia's crimes against Ukraine. But I can't speak with them without feeling anger somewhere deep inside me, so I try not to speak to them at all. Thinking about how they have closed their eyes to what Putin and his people are doing, without doing anything against it, makes me feel sick.

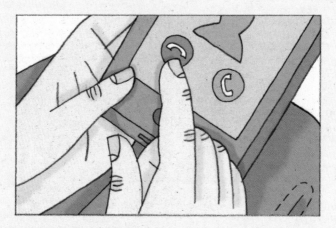

This week I was waiting to hear back from a friend who lives in Severodonetsk, a region that's under constant shelling from the Russians. He's an activist and very open about his anti-Russian views, so I was worried. I knew that if the Russians captured him, they would torture and kill him. When I finally heard back from him it was such a relief. He somehow escaped that hell. I hope to see him in Kyiv. I'll return to Ukraine this week.

I'm still in Riga. People here seem open, friendly and trustworthy. Sometimes I worry that some won't want to talk to me or work with me because I am Russian. I haven't seen this happen, so I hope these are just my own internal fears.

There used to be many negative stereotypes in the world about Russians. I was very glad when that perception gradually changed over the years. But now we're going backwards, and there will be new negative stereotypes. I have read comments about canceling Russian culture. It is difficult for me to read such comments, but I try to understand the people who write them. I can't even begin to imagine what they experience and feel. But I also know that not all Ukrainians think this way.

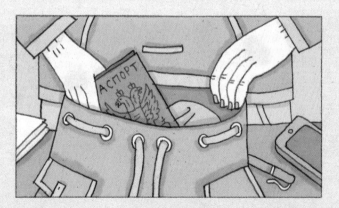

I have collaborated with a French institute over the years, and they have offered to help with my visa application. A French visa would allow me and my family and I to stay in Latvia for ninety days because it is valid anywhere in the European Union. I'll return to Russia this week for the paperwork.

I am back in Lviv. My kids have gotten used to my traveling back and forth between Copenhagen and Ukraine. My oldest son is now in school and I think it gives him something very important: a feeling that he's not alone. I've also gotten used to my constant traveling. When I'm in transit in Warsaw or Budapest I feel almost at home.

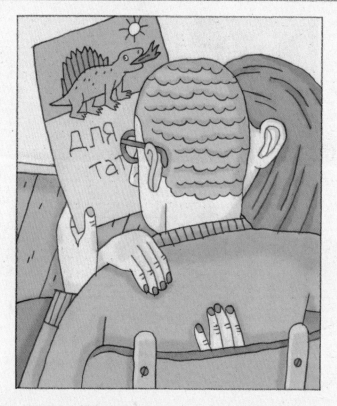

My husband dreams about seeing the kids! Not seeing them is the only thing that unsettles him. He is relieved that they are in a safe place but at the same time he misses them so much that he would do anything to see them. They miss him too, of course.
We have plans to temporarily reunite this summer.
Maybe in Ukraine, maybe elsewhere in Europe.

I plan to return to Kyiv tomorrow, but it'll depend on fuel — we have a petrol shortage across Ukraine. I have some interviews there, then I'll go to the eastern or southern regions to report. I really want to know what's going on there. I've been to the Donbas region many times before, and I think I can report more deeply on it than most international journalists.
It's the frontline, but I feel fearless.

I arrived back in St. Petersburg last Sunday. I was asked no questions at the border, and I arrived back home at midnight. The first one to greet me was my dog. My children were already asleep, but my wife was waiting up for me. The next morning, the kids hugged me, and I gave them toys I bought for them in Latvia, and shirts from H&M, which has closed down in Russia. I can cook pancakes and omelets for the kids for breakfast, and read them Russian detective stories before bedtime again.

The city looks transformed to me. Everything is green. I feel a sense of unfamiliarity because there are no Ukrainian flags displayed. Instead, I've noticed subway posters featuring the letter Z. I've come to understand that thinking about the possibility of being denounced for my political views has become part of my Russian identity. It worries me because it reminds me of what happened during Soviet times.

Getting my papers notarized for Latvia will take a long time. I often worry that we won't be able to actualize our plans.

A couple of days ago I woke up to the sound of explosions close to my apartment here in Kyiv. I could even smell the smoke. It felt like the first day of the war.

I recently spoke to my mother about our cultural identity. She considers herself Ukrainian, but she is really Russian-Jewish. My parents and grandparents grew up in the Volga region, close to Ukraine. My granddad always referred to our family as Cossack, rather than Russian. He often told me stories about the Cossack village where he was born.

He also knew a lot of Ukrainian folk songs. During the occupation of Crimea and the Donbas region, Russian authorities created a fake movement, allegedly run by Cossacks against protesters whom they attacked and tortured. My grandfather was so mad when he heard about this "Cossack movement." He said that it had nothing to do with his own Cossack roots.

I never considered myself Russian either, even though I grew up in Russia. When I was thirteen, my mother and I moved to Ukraine because she remarried in Crimea. I attended a Ukrainian school and later returned to Russia to study at university and begin my career as a journalist there. After a few years in Russia, I moved back to Ukraine. When I received my Ukrainian citizenship I gave up my Russian passport.

Today, I'm heading to the eastern frontline to report.

Yesterday I asked my nine-year-old what patriotism means. He said he doesn't know. Then I asked him what the term "native land" means. He said that it's the place where you were born. When I asked whether the notion of your native land can change when you move to another place, he said it wouldn't.

I don't have a clear idea of what Russian cultural identity means. I have Siberian and Jewish ancestors. I was born in the Soviet Union, but I grew up in Russia. I'm against the war, so in the eyes of the Russian government I am a traitor. But in the eyes of foreign people, I am Russian, a citizen of the country that started the war. I feel as if St. Petersburg is my country. When someone asks me where I'm from I tell them St. Petersburg instead of Russia. When I first traveled abroad in 2006 and told people where I was from, all they associated with Russia was snow, bears and organized crime.

Then I saw that perception change. But now we're back again where we started. I would describe Russians, at least those who love art and literature, as open to new ideas, positive and passionate about helping others. But maybe that's just my imagination.

I'm in my hometown right now, visiting my mother with the kids. I read about a state-organized funeral that took place here a few days ago for a twenty-year-old soldier who died in Ukraine. The echo of the war will be felt everywhere in Russia. There will be many graves.

My reporting team and I returned to Kyiv from the Donbas region yesterday. Tomorrow we will go to the frontline in Sloviansk. Donbas feels like home to me. I spent so much time there before the invasion. For the past eight years, ever since Russia's last attack, people there have been rebuilding their cities. New communities emerged that created comfortable living spaces. Now their dreams are broken again. I saw so many tanks, soldiers and rescue teams. When speaking to people there, it occurred to me that tomorrow or next week they may be killed in another attack. I heard dozens of explosions within the course of just two hours and asked myself why I am so calm when Russian rockets land so close to us. It's because we have been at war for more than three months, and we are used to it.

I interviewed a local administrator in a town very close to the frontline. The city is surprisingly well groomed. Rose bushes are everywhere. Locals walk the streets with children, teenagers ride their scooters. It looks peaceful, but it isn't safe. The administrator told me about people who are being buried in their own backyards. Heavy artillery in the region tears people to pieces, a hand may be lying here, a head over there. Bodies lie unburied for several days because it is impossible to take them away. Sometimes neighbors come out to bury the bodies and are themselves killed by the shelling.

We're having problems with our visa documents and have to prepare everything all over again. I was told that it will take until the end of next month to get some of my documents notarized. But we have become calmer about it all and have decided to go through with our plan without too much unnecessary stress.

A close friend of mine organizes concerts in Russia. Last week, he had an appointment at the office of the St. Petersburg Committee for Culture to speak about the delay of one of his concerts. He was shown a list that included the names of some of his musicians who are now banned from performing by the Russian government because they are against the war and speak out about it publicly.

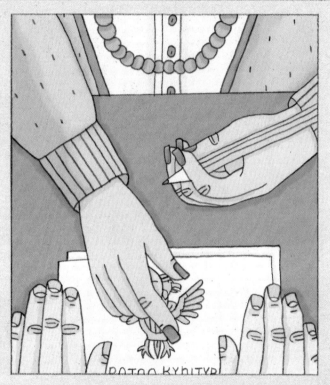

Discrediting the Russian army is forbidden by law. Almost any statement or action against the war can be seen as criticizing the army, in which case you can face a fine or a prison sentence of up to ten years. Two of my friend's performances got delayed because of this ban. He is worried about his career and his own safety and is thinking about immigrating to Serbia or Georgia. But he also has a family, which makes it complicated.

Now it's summer — but do I have the right to feel the summer vibe?

I'm at the frontline in the south of Ukraine and I hear explosions all the time, boom after boom after boom. But life goes on and people here are very supportive of each other. They had to live without water for a few days, and they lack electricity, medicine and food (wheat is the new gold!). They live in hell, and they want to win this war so badly. Hundreds of pro-Ukrainian activists here were taken prisoner. I spoke to some of the soldiers stationed here. They are smart, courageous and have a great sense of humor.

The zoo in Mykolaiv was hit by cluster bombs. The Russians shelled it at least eight times. Luckily, no one was hit. I don't understand why anyone would want to shell a zoo. The zoo in Kharkiv was also bombed some months ago, and many animals and three caretakers were killed. Mykolaiv's zoo director proudly showed me a photograph of himself and Princess Diana, who once visited this zoo. The zoo is his life, and now it is in great danger. I've never been this close to a giraffe.

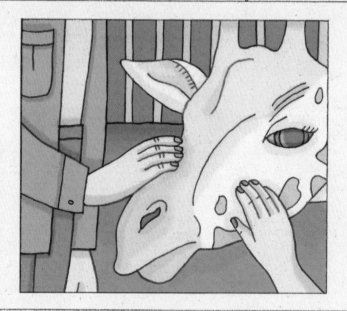

I met a woman named Elena in Sloviansk. "Do you need a car?" she asked me, laughing, and pointed at a burnt-out wreck on the street. "Its owner told me he doesn't need it anymore." Her house was shelled a few days ago. It happened in the middle of the night, but luckily she wasn't hit. Three of her neighbors died in the attack. Almost everything in her house got destroyed, but one vase survived. "I look after the bombed apartments here so that they don't get looted. There are many marauders here," she told me.

I drove to Riga from Moscow with some friends. This time we came via Belarus. We weren't required to show any special documents and made our way to Latvia quickly. Maybe I'll use the same route when I bring my family.

Last year, Belarusians protested against their president. I followed the protests in the news. I hoped the Belarusian people would succeed, but unfortunately things only got worse. One of my Belarusian friends, a music producer who took part in the protests, ended up in prison where he was tortured. After his release, he escaped to Georgia where he now lives and organizes music events. On the drive through Belarus, I tried to find traces of the attempted revolution. But all I could see were endless fields of wheat.

Last Friday I went to the concert of a Belarusian band. I've known them for more than ten years because my close friend used to organize concerts for them in St. Petersburg. Right after the war started, they canceled all their concerts in Russia, refusing to perform there. Now they are touring Poland and the Baltics.

I still don't know what to do about my future. I regularly experience a state of confusion. Last weekend I was in Vilnius, Lithuania. It's a beautiful city, and many people there speak Russian. But I continue to feel unsettled, knowing that I'm from Russia, the country that unleashed this war.

Last week was intense. I interviewed people in Mykolaiv, and I observed the State Emergency Service's fascinating work. They de-mine houses and fields all over the region, 24/7. I spent one whole day with them during which they found six bombs and parts of Russian Uragan rockets. One of the team members handed me the projectile of one of the bombs. It felt heavy and hot because it's over 40 degrees Celsius outside at the moment.

I spoke to a farmer who, despite the war, has to continue harvesting his fields. During our interview, Ukrainian troops launched a few rockets towards the Russian side, only 200 meters away from us. The farmer just shrugged it off. "Nothing out of the ordinary," he said. "They're just defending us." Then we had to get away quickly because we expected the Russians to fire back — but they didn't. I guess I'm very lucky.

I worry that one day Ukraine will run out of weapons because the allies hesitated too long, and Russia will kill thousands more. A few days ago, they launched rockets into Kyiv again. They hit a house close to my friend's apartment building, but she is safe.

I found out that Denmark will provide me and my family with a two-year residence permit, as well as an apartment, which feels like a great privilege. Now I'm at the Polish border, heading back to Copenhagen. I'll see my kids again and bring them to Ukraine with me for a vacation. They haven't seen their father and their grandparents for four months, ever since the war began. We decided to gather somewhere in a relatively quiet and safe place.

This week, Latvians are celebrating Līgo, Midsummer Eve. It's very hot in Riga and I spent some time at the beach. I don't know why, but this time, as soon as I arrived here, I started missing my family very much, much more so than the last time I came to Riga. I tried to find a hotel near the sea where I could bring them for a vacation. I could introduce Latvia to our children this way. And I'm hoping that spending time outside of Russia will help us relax a little.

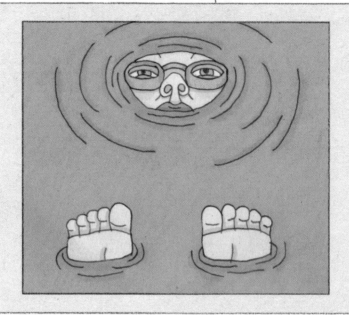

Last week my wife was at the visa application center. They accepted her documents, so we are hoping she'll receive her visa in one or two weeks' time. One of my best friends is immigrating to France with her husband, their two children and their dog. She had a goodbye party in St. Petersburg, and I participated online.

I read an interview with the director of St. Petersburg's art museum, the Hermitage. In the interview, he described the museum's recent exhibitions abroad as "cultural offensives" against those countries, as "special operations." He said: "We are no longer retreating, we've made a turn," and "We're all militarists and imperialists. Our country is changing world history." It's terrible. I can't stop thinking about it, and I can't believe he could say things like that. I met him once in person a few years ago at an exhibition that we collaborated on. It's really hard for me to read his words.

I'm in Copenhagen, and it's calm and beautiful here. But imagine waking up, going to the city center to buy groceries and suddenly being hit and killed by a missile. That's what Ukrainians are afraid of every day. How many more rockets does Putin have lined up for Ukraine? How many experts, institutes and think tanks have studied Russia for decades? Hundreds? Thousands? And yet, most of them were surprised when Russia invaded Ukraine. Most experts never studied Russian colonialism. It's a blind spot.

Not much has changed since the beginning of the invasion. Ukraine is trying to hold on, but the price is extraordinarily high. It's hard to imagine what life is like in the occupied areas. People there have been waiting to be liberated for more than four months. They don't have proper food, water or money. Hundreds were kidnapped and taken to prisons, tortured or even killed. For them, the sound of artillery would be a relief.

The most frustrating thing for me is that I don't know where to live. Many Ukrainians probably struggle with the same question. My kids are in Copenhagen while I work in Ukraine, traveling back and forth between different warzones. But I have good news: My husband, his parents, the kids and I are heading to a guest house in the Carpathian Mountains where we'll spend a short vacation together as a family. We're absolutely happy.

Yesterday I arrived back in St. Petersburg. It's hot here, more than 30 degrees Celsius. There are many people in the streets. Everyone is looking happy and carefree. People sit in sidewalk bars and restaurants and eat and drink. It feels as if there is no war going on. I read the news about the Ukrainian bombing of Belgorod, a Russian city near the border. It's terrible, but this is exactly what war is like. This isn't just a "special operation."

Two nights ago, I had an apocalyptic dream. I was walking with someone in a field. Suddenly the sky ripped open — it just broke apart. I woke up, and it was early morning.

The Russian borders have reopened. From now on, I don't have to show any foreign work permits for proof when leaving Russia for another country. My wife and I have been discussing our emigration plans. She thinks it'll be best if I get a work permit for Latvia first, while she stays in Russia with the children. She would like them to remain in school in St. Petersburg for the time being. But we are worried they might be taught propaganda in school. The Russian government announced that it is introducing new lessons, special educational programs on patriotism. But what does that mean, exactly?

I'm in Zakarpattia, the Carpathian Mountains, with my husband, his parents and our kids. Before WWII, this area was a territory of Hungary. The villages close to the guesthouse were built in the 13th and 14th centuries. It's beautiful and peaceful here. My parents-in-law are visiting this area for the first time, and they like it very much. The guesthouse has a swimming pool, so my kids spend most of their time in the water.

Before we arrived, I told my family that this would be the safest place for us to gather because Russia wouldn't shell this region: It's close to Hungary and Hungary's prime minister is Putin's friend. But during our second night, we were woken by the sound of an air raid siren. My husband's parents said they heard the hissing sound of a flying rocket. They believe it was a cruise missile. They know this sound very well because they often hear such sounds in Kyiv, where they live. They weren't scared at all.

Today, Russia fired missiles at a crowded neighborhood in Vinnytsia. A little girl was killed, and this news crushed me. The girl's mother survived the attack, but is in hospital with multiple injuries. The doctors haven't told her yet that her daughter is dead — they worry that if they did, she'd lose her will to live, and die. The girl was the same age as my younger son. I watched a video of her and cried. What if this woman were me, and this child mine? Would I support Ukraine's surrender, just so all of this would end?

I seem to have returned to normal life this week. I get up at 7:30 AM, walk the dog, make breakfast for the children and go grocery shopping. I took part in a charity book sale event in support of people with disabilities. Many people donated books. I helped unload them from a van, and there were at least four tons. There were a lot of supportive people at the event, and I'm sure that many of these people are against the war. It was a very emotional experience for me.

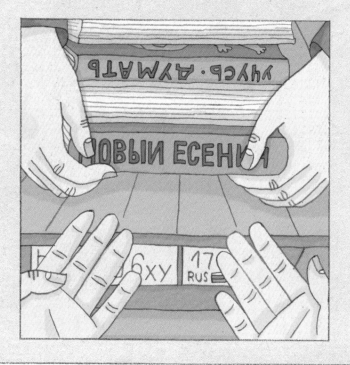

The place where Russian culture is most actively canceled is in Russia itself. Many Russian writers and musicians have by now been banned by the Russian authorities, and a week ago, three theater directors were fired. I asked my wife whether she is more scared by the idea of staying in Russia, or by the idea of emigrating. She said it is scarier for her to leave because she is afraid that she will feel alone and without a real purpose. I am afraid too.

There were new explosions in Ukraine today, in Vinnitsa. I have no words to describe those horrors. People continue to die. I feel dumb with despair, paralyzed. And I understand that, no matter where I end up living, I will feel this way. I can change my location, but I cannot change that feeling.

I've left the kids with their grandparents and my husband at our vacation rental in the Carpathian Mountains, in the countryside of Ukraine, to go to Ternopil in western Ukraine, where I'll be attending a friend's wedding. I hope the ceremony won't be interrupted by sirens or missiles.

Ukraine never was a very open state because it was part of the Soviet system for so long, and the Soviet Union itself was anti-Semitic. I've heard many anti-Semitic jokes in Ukraine. I've also witnessed many attacks on human rights defenders, left-wing activists and LGBT people by far-right groups. I used to attend LGBT pride events in Kyiv, and each time I saw right-wing radicals attacking participants, some wielding bats. Sometimes the police interfered, other times they didn't. Some of the attackers wore tattoos of swastikas and Adolf Hitler. Personally, I don't know anyone who likes such symbols, but I prefer to judge people by their deeds, not their tattoos. It's the violence that I abhor.

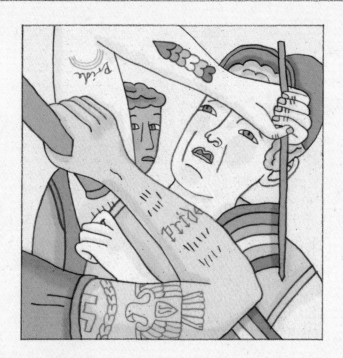

What Putin has done is blame those kinds of radicals to justify his aggression and Russia's invasion. He even accused our Jewish president of being a Nazi. The Russian authorities are liars and indifferent to what the world thinks of them. This invasion cannot be justified by anything.

Life goes on, but now it's accompanied by a constant sense of grief. I don't understand yet how to live with this feeling. How to regain confidence. How to talk to my children in a way that doesn't scare them. My daily work routine helps. Being around the people I love also helps, of course. And yesterday I went for a walk in my neighborhood in St. Petersburg, which helped a little, too.

Using the word "denazification" for what is currently going on in Ukraine is a crazy form of propaganda. Of course there are also Nazis in Russia, just like anywhere else in the world. I read about street fights and acts of violence from time to time, mostly against Asian people from the former Soviet Republics, but also others.

Seventeen years ago, a friend of a friend of mine was attacked by neo-Nazis in the street for his antifascist views. His name was Timur Kacharava. He was twenty years old. They stabbed him to death. His friends testified that he had previously received death threats. I didn't know him very well, but I used to see him from time to time at local bars. He was fun to talk to. After it happened, I visited the place where he had been killed. There were flowers and a sign that read "Timur, we will always remember you." That was probably my closest encounter with Nazism in Russia.

Oh, it felt so good to gather with my friends at last week's wedding, all of whom now live in different places. Since I work mostly in the war zones I don't usually get to see any of my friends — I just don't have the time for that, which is sad.

I'm in Mykolayiv in the south of Ukraine right now. People here are used to the constant shelling, but it has its consequences. A psychiatrist who works at the hospital here told me that local people come to him every day, complaining about panic attacks.

I was at the frontline this morning, just 4 kilometers from the Russian positions, and 24 kilometers from occupied Kherson where lots of my friends lived before the invasion. I was shown around by a military officer who happens to be originally from Crimea, which is close to here. I told him I lived there before its annexation, and he asked what street I used to live on. I suddenly felt crushed.

I remember every inch of that street, every house, every tree, every flower bed. It's a strange feeling to see the territories that you know so well now occupied, and to not be able to return to them. Crimea is the best place on Earth for me, and I dream about returning to it, to see my old friends, to enter the house where I lived, to visit my grandparents' graves. I want to touch its earth and its trees. I can't return to the place that feels like my own fingerprint. Being this close to it today without being able to see it made me very emotional.

A few days ago, we went to the Gulf of Finland with some friends by minibus. We built a bonfire, grilled sausages and flew a kite. I didn't read the news all day.

Next week, I'll find out whether I can get my university diploma officially certified by Russia, to be granted specialist status and receive a work permit in Latvia. Without this permit, our European Union visa allows us to stay in Latvia for only ninety days. Our plan is to go to Latvia for a short vacation with the kids and to submit our papers while there. The children can't wait. They're most looking forward to swimming in the sea, and to finally being able to eat at McDonald's and buy Lego and Nintendo games again.

My wife and I talked about a route for emigrating with our dog. We don't have a car, and dogs aren't allowed on buses. We don't want to leave without her. The only way to make it work would be to rent a car and drive to the border of Estonia, cross the border by foot, walk to the next train station and take a train to Tallinn — and then to rent a car to drive to Riga.

I've noticed a new kind of poster in St. Petersburg. Photo portraits of Russian soldiers who are fighting in Ukraine. The posters call them heroes, but they're not my heroes. I'm still feeling depressed. It's a strange feeling: In the morning I am okay, and after a few hours I can't do anything. Psychotherapy has become more and more popular in Russia over the years. I might need a specialist at some point, but I'm not ready yet.

Ukrainian nights aren't quiet: Around 3 or 4 AM you are woken up by sirens, then you hear heavy shelling somewhere nearby, then you watch the air defense from your window. After that, if you can, you fall back asleep. Yet Ukrainian nights are also beautiful. During the curfew, there are no lights in the streets and you see all the stars. After spending almost a week at the frontline, I slept like a child in Kyiv even during the air raid alarms.

Today I'm back at the Carpathian Mountains, where my children have spent the last few weeks with their father. I'm preparing to take them back to Denmark. I feel sadness and relief at the same time. Denmark is one of the best countries in the world for kids. It's safe and beautiful. But for us as a family it's tough. My husband feels frustrated and sad. He wants to be with our kids every day. He was so happy spending time with them during his stay here in the countryside. Now he can't see them again for months. It's painful to accept that we can't live together as a family anymore.

I think my seven-year-old has grown up quickly since the war began. Now we talk about existential questions, about war and peace, cultural identity, about roots. He is wiser now, and he can take care of his little brother. He has become more responsible. In bed last night, he told my husband that he didn't want to fall asleep because then he would be closer to the day of his departure back to Denmark, and that he doesn't want to have to flee his own country.

I asked my children if they thought that our relationship has changed since the beginning of the war, and they said no. The only difference is that we never used the word "war" when talking to each other before.

I told the children early on that it was Putin who started the war, that Russia invaded Ukraine, that I'm against the war and that Ukraine is a great country. I told them about the bombs, and about people having to take refuge in subway tunnels. They know that the war continues, but I've stopped talking to them about it. I don't want to tell them about its horrors every day. During the first weeks, they saw videos of the war which occasionally appeared in between the shows that they were watching on YouTube. Our younger one told us about them, the older one didn't.

When such clips popped up, they closed their eyes or pushed the phone away. I don't believe they think that much about the war these days. The only times they mention it is in the context of wanting things they can't have because of the sanctions.

One day, my younger kid came home from school and said that a student had mentioned that it was Ukraine that had attacked Russia. We explained that this isn't true. If I get a sense that propaganda is being taught at school, I'd want my children to grow up in a different country. I will be fine with them living in a culture different from my own. I want them to become part of the larger culture of the world.

I am back in Denmark with the kids and my mother. We've moved into social housing. Many Ukrainian families live here, together with migrants from the Middle East. We call it "our nice ghetto," because the Ukrainians here always help each other out. I wouldn't call myself a "refugee" because I haven't applied for asylum. I wouldn't say that my mother and children are refugees either. The term that's used for us here is simply "Ukrainians." Everyone thinks that we'll go back to Ukraine when the war is over. We think so too, but we'll see. For now, I'm here until the beginning of September. I'll go and see some art museums while I'm here in Copenhagen. It's a great opportunity to learn more about this part of the world. Still, for me, it's easier to work in the field, even when it's dangerous, than to sit around quietly in Denmark with the children.

I've been thinking about how the war has affected my body. I feel that I'm getting older. Soon after the invasion began, I noticed new wrinkles around my eyes. My friends look different, too. Their skin is paler than it was before, their eyes have gotten darker and their passion for life is gone. I'm afraid of aging, and I think I'll end up looking much older than my actual age. I'm afraid that I'll die too early because my body can't handle the trauma I've had to go through. I think that many Ukrainians experience something like this. We spend so much time struggling, resisting and fighting. What for? There are so many beautiful things in the world. But tyrants, driven by madness, destroy them.

My children and I entered Latvia yesterday via a small border crossing in the forest. I heard that at some checkpoints at the Latvian border, Russian immigrants are being asked to sign a document that condemns the war. That way, they try to identify people who may pose a threat to Latvia's national security. I understand it, but it feels strange. I haven't been asked to sign such a form, but if they ask me to, I will.

There are Ukrainian flags displayed everywhere here on buildings, in windows and on the doors of buses. My younger kid thinks there are too many and, while driving through the streets of Riga, said: "It seems to me that we aren't in Latvia, but in Ukraine. There are more Ukrainian flags here than Latvian ones!"
"No, we are in Latvia," the older one said. "There are this many Ukrainian flags here because Latvia is against the war."

After checking in at the hotel, we visited McDonald's. I'm not a big fan. I only eat there because my kids like it. We visited a video game museum and bought some new Nintendo games. The kids were very happy. In a few days, we'll go to a village near the Gulf of Riga, where my wife will join us. My plan is to introduce the kids to Riga over the course of the next few days, and then to ask them how they would feel about staying here for a longer period. I haven't allowed myself to think that much about the idea of Latvia becoming their new home. Maybe my mind is blocking these kinds of thoughts.

I went to a museum in Copenhagen with the kids yesterday that had an excellent collection of 19th-century art. As I was looking at paintings featuring landscapes and cities, I felt frustrated. We live in such a different world today. So many cities are destroyed. Nature has been defiled. There is so much hatred, so many wars across the globe. Humanity has failed at preserving the most beautiful things. How did we ever get to this point?

The other day, the gaps between the leaves of the tree in my friend's backyard in Copenhagen looked to me like a Z. I see imaginary Zs everywhere. I constantly feel anxious. I'm afraid that something will happen to my friends or relatives. Even small things that, at other times, would have never bothered me, now get stuck in my head. Someone sent me a parcel, but I wasn't home. I kept thinking that it would be a disaster if I couldn't find anyone to pick it up. I try to push those fears away, but it doesn't work.

I have real concerns about what the winter will look like. What if Ukrainians won't have electricity or gas? My husband decided to rent a house in Lviv with a woodburning oven, so we won't freeze to death. It's a big house, and our plan is to host our friends there, in case their heating stops working. We've decided to give up our apartment in Kyiv. I never used to like these kinds of apartment blocks very much: tall, big and empty. But now I don't want to move from there. I have so many things: books, photographs, paintings, clothes, furniture. I can't imagine moving everything so suddenly.

We're having a vacation on the Gulf of Riga, where we're sunbathing and swimming in the warm water. My wife arrived here yesterday. We're staying at a guesthouse together with a couple of Lithuanian tourists. Yesterday we made kebab together, and they treated me to Ukrainian vodka. We talked about the war. They said they couldn't understand why Russia started the war. I told them that I think the war is evil.

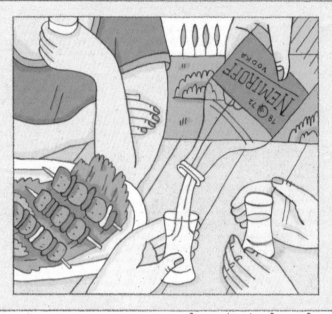

Yesterday was the anniversary of the death of the famous Soviet musician Viktor Tsoi. I was a big fan of his as a teenager. He died in a car crash thirty-two years ago near the village where we're staying. There is a monument at the crash site which we went to by bicycle. A lot of people were there, and his songs blasted from loudspeakers in Russian. He was against the Soviet regime, and his song "Khochu Peremen (I Want Change)" became a symbol for change, including during the Belarusian protests of 2020.

We read the news about the European Union's potential visa ban on Russians. This could mean that soon we won't be able to emigrate from Russia. We're talking about other options. The problem is that I can't make any plans. I can only think ahead for a week or two. I'm trying to live in the moment rather than the future.

Yesterday I took my seven-year-old to the Viking Ship Museum in Copenhagen — he was very excited. A Mexican band performed on the street near the museum. When the performance ended, the band's leader spoke into his microphone and said, "Stop wars everywhere!" I thought about how senseless this kind of comment is. It's like advising a homeless person to buy a house.

My friends on Crimea have been seeing contrails from Ukrainian air defense missiles in the sky. Only two weeks ago, I asked them to move out of Crimea, to a safer place, because I knew that the counteroffensive would begin. And it did begin. I hope they'll be fine. It's very hard to see my beloved Crimea under attack, but it's necessary because it's even harder to see the Russian army destroy my country.

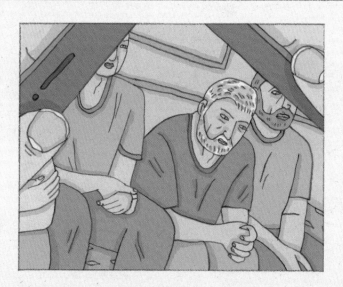

There are peaceful ways of resisting totalitarianism: You can raise awareness about what's going on, find allies worldwide, build a network of people who can help in small ways. Or you can take up arms and fight. Today, Russian propagandists released a video of my friend Max Butkevych, a human rights activist who is in Russian captivity. Max is a pacifist. He fought peacefully for human rights and equality all his life. But when Russia invaded Ukraine, the only option he saw was to join the army. You can't fix this kind of problem without weapons. Max got caught by the Russians near Severodonetsk. In the video, his hair looks all gray, and he looks very thin. It was painful to see him like that, but I'm glad that he's alive.

Our beach vacation is over. We had a great time swimming, walking in the forest and drinking wine. There were times when I forgot all about the war. Now my wife and children are back in Russia, and I've returned to Riga where I'll stay for another week, to sell and ship some of my artwork. I've started reading the news about the war again, and I'm not feeling so good.

I think that the Ukrainian counteroffensive will have a mental impact on the Russian people. Russians went to the beach in Crimea, hoping for a vacation, and instead they got bombs. I hope that at least they understand now that this is not just a military operation, but a real war. I'm afraid of what would happen if bombs were dropped on St. Petersburg. But I try to see it from the Ukrainian perspective, and I can understand why they would bomb Russia. There are a lot of discussions about the possibility of Russia attacking the Baltic states, and I've wondered what would happen if Riga were bombed while I am here.

Last night I met a man from the UK who's returning to Moscow to be with his Russian wife. I asked why he's going to the country that started this war. He told me that his own country has been involved in many wars as an aggressor. I found his answer strange — at the same time I accept it because I realize that I have no idea about what British people think about wars that involve their own people.

Гор. Сумы. Iя Женская Гимназія.

Summer — Fall

Some of my friends were captured by the Russians. Some will die serving in the army. Some are already dead. When I hear people say that Ukraine is asking for too much, I feel helpless.

Some time ago, my husband and I were discussing what kinds of skills we should learn now that our country is at war. Before Russia's invasion we discussed the issue of owning a gun many times. Every time we agreed that owning a gun means being willing to actually shoot someone. I myself can't imagine killing a human being, not even in the name of defending my country.

A few months ago, we were interviewing soldiers at a military base in southern Ukraine. With the permission of the soldiers, my cameraman picked up a gun and started shooting at a target. I heard a ringing sound as he fired the bullets. I was invited to shoot at a target as well, but I told the soldiers that I didn't feel prepared to shoot. My husband also refused. But now he says he's ready to go to a shooting range and practice. I think it's a good idea for him to learn new skills that would be useful at times of war. But I still can't imagine owning a gun or killing someone — I value human life too much.

I don't ask myself what I'd be willing to die for. I simply plan not to die. My goal is to survive, to help other people survive this war and to preserve the Ukrainian heritage.

I went from Latvia to Estonia by bus. At Narva, I crossed the border to Russia by foot across a bridge. When I entered Ivangorod, the first town on the Russian side, I saw no signs of war. People went about their daily business, children played at the playground. It was only when I was back in the subway of St. Petersburg that I saw posters with the letter Z on them.

Over the past four months, I've entered Russia three times. When I crossed the bridge this time, I was thinking about whether I could really move out of Russia. Visa sanctions are still being discussed, and Russians with Estonian visas are already barred from reentering Estonia.

And this time, when I returned to St. Petersburg, I felt a more acute sense that I had come home. Even the most banal things, such as throwing out my garbage, going to the grocery store or walking my dog, evoked strong feelings of belonging. Imagining leaving Russia is becoming more difficult for me.

I thought about what would happen if I were drafted, and I've decided that I would refuse to carry a weapon. I'm ready to go to prison if that's the price I have to pay. It was the Russian government that started this war, and I cannot see myself fighting on their side. If Russia had been invaded by another country, however, I think I would have been willing to carry a weapon. I'd be willing to die for my family.

Today is the first day of school in Ukraine. Only thirty percent of all children there are able to go back to class because of the frequent shelling of school buildings. Many schools now have bomb shelters. In the occupied areas, Russian soldiers intimidate teachers and parents, loot equipment and banish Ukrainian history and culture from the curriculum. Before the invasion, I planned to celebrate my oldest son's first school day in Kyiv. Now he'll go to school here in Copenhagen. He told me that he misses Kyiv, that he feels sad that he can't see his father and his grandparents and that he loves them very much. I try not to cry when I hear things like that, but it's tough. We didn't choose this new life for ourselves — Russia stole our old one.

A friend of mine evacuated her family to Germany from Kyiv. Her son was going to attend school there, but the city they immigrated to is overwhelmed with migrants. For an entire month, she got up early every day to visit schools and ask for a place for her son. Every day she got a rejection. She's working as a waitress to earn a living, and now she also has to homeschool her son. The boy's father is back in Ukraine. I'm grateful that my kids have school and preschool, that they have a grandmother and a nanny. But what I miss is a sense of family. I used to be together with my husband almost all the time, and now that I'm in Denmark, we can only talk over the phone. I haven't seen him for more than a month, and I don't know if he'll be allowed to leave Ukraine. I hope we'll see each other soon.

It's September and we took the children back to school in St. Petersburg. There's a new class on the curriculum, called "Talking About the Important Things." In this class, the kids listened to the national anthem and learned about Russia's, England's and America's coats of arms. The government recently decided that students in Russia must salute the flag and schools must play the national anthem every week. They did this at our kids' school on orientation day as well, and it felt strange. The anthem was played for only thirty seconds and turned off in the middle, after which the school's own hymn was played without interruption. My kids don't know the lyrics to the national anthem. They didn't sing along.

I learned the anthem of the USSR in elementary school. Everyone had to memorize it. Mine was the last generation that joined the Young Pioneers, the state youth organization. I joined one spring, and by the fall, the organization had dissolved. After the collapse of the USSR, Russia adopted a new anthem. When Putin became president, he changed it back to the one from the USSR, with minor changes. The Soviet anthem was important to me as a child, but now it just sounds fake. The only time I ever felt pride when seeing the Russian flag was when our team won during the Olympic Games. Flags used to be displayed only on Russian holidays. Now they're on many buildings, but I don't see them in people's windows. Ever since the beginning of the war, the red stripe on the bottom of the flag has made me think of blood.

I've been in Copenhagen for over a month, visiting the kids. Several times this week, I found myself crying about seemingly unimportant things. This is unusual for me. I tell myself that I must hold on, to keep my sanity, and to help myself and others survive. I know that the work we do as war journalists is very important, so I have to keep on going, no matter what. I don't have the right to fall apart. If you asked me about the most important Ukrainian character trait, I'd say that it's just that: You fall down, you get back up and you keep on going. We have no other option but to pull ourselves out of the swamp by our own hair.

I wept because a friend of mine in Ukraine told me that he enlisted for military service. I never thought he would, but he did. This week we received the good news from the Kharkiv region, and when I saw videos of the towns liberated from Russian occupation, I cried again. One of the videos showed a Ukrainian soldier ripping a Russian propaganda poster off a billboard. Underneath, an old poster appeared that featured a quote about freedom by the Ukrainian poet Taras Shevchenko. It was so touching to see.

My seven-year-old son cried last week, too. He spoke on the phone to his father, who is in Kyiv. When he saw my husband on the screen, he started sobbing and telling him that he wants to go back home, that he loves Ukraine and that he misses our family being together. This week, my husband's mother will come from Kyiv to visit us here in Denmark. I think that'll make him feel better.

I just came back from the grocery store here in St. Petersburg. On the way home, I noticed people in military uniforms. They were actors shooting a film about WWII. The streets were filled with anti-tank hedgehogs made of wood. How strange it is to shoot a war movie at this time. I wonder what those "soldiers" carrying uniforms and guns think about the current war.

There was a parent-teacher meeting at my children's school this week. We were told that a new lesson will be taught each Monday before the first class, during which teachers will discuss things like the Russian flag and anthem. I was the only parent who asked questions. Then the teacher said that attending the new class isn't mandatory. "You understand that this lesson was imposed on us by the ministry of education," she said. This propaganda project doesn't appear to be very successful.

Growing up in Russia in the 1990s, I felt that I could express my opinions openly. That changed under Putin. As a young man, I wasn't very political. My focus was my work, although I tried to change the negative perception of Russia abroad by bringing international artists to St. Petersburg. Now I ask myself if my entire generation made a mistake by not paying enough attention to politics. It's important that the next generation be involved in shaping our government. I told my children about the importance of a free press, and about the fake news that has been spread about this war. I didn't tell them not to mention these conversations in public. I've decided not to worry about that.

I have great news: My husband was allowed to leave Ukraine. He got special permission from the Ukrainian Ministry of Culture because we'll be attending the ceremony of a European journalism prize for which we are nominated. He joined us in Copenhagen last week, and he'll be here with us for a month. His mother is here, too — almost our entire family is reunited. I hadn't told my seven-year-old son that his father was going to come, so it was a big surprise for him. My husband rang the bell, my son opened the door and when he saw his father, he screamed with joy, jumped into his arms and hugged him for a long time.

We spent the weekend showing my husband our favorite places. We went to Tivoli Gardens, Copenhagen's amusement park, and got on some wild rides. Then we explored the aquarium and the city center together. My husband is so happy to be here, and in safety. It's a great relief. It's his first time outside Ukraine this year. He experienced so much stress there, and now he is finally able to rest. Most men in Ukraine must be experiencing a huge amount of stress because they aren't allowed to leave Ukraine at all, not even for a week, to experience a sense of safety.

Having my husband here is a great relief for me too. Looking after the kids, working hard and repairing things around the apartment has made me so tired. At the same time I miss Ukraine, especially my fieldwork. I would like to be in Severodonetsk and in Mariupol the moment they are being liberated.

Yesterday, Russia's most famous singer, Alla Pugacheva, wrote about the war on Instagram. She said that Russia's soldiers are "dying for illusory aims that make our country a pariah." She didn't write about the effect the war has had on Ukraine. Nonetheless, I think she found very good words that will resonate with Russians. I hope her post will cause more people here to think about the fact that Russian soldiers are dying for nothing. All the independent Russian media wrote about her post.

For the first time since the beginning of the war, I decided to fix up some of the broken items in our apartment. We have a tap in the kitchen that has been leaking for a long time, and I replaced it. A strange feeling overcame me at the hardware store, and I was thinking: "While Ukraine is being destroyed, there are many people at this store who are buying materials to fix something that's broken." I was one of those people.

I'm not used to being around that many people anymore. I've been isolating myself from others more and more. I only want to spend time with individuals I trust and with whom I share the same views. I've started spending more time with the children — playing Nintendo games, going for walks, cooking the food that they like. I think I'm trying to find peace of mind through my children. But I don't anticipate that feeling lasting for long.

My husband is still in Copenhagen with us. He is doing very well. Today, he and I and the kids were in Sweden, which is very close to Copenhagen. We went to a few art museums there. It feels great to experience different facets of European history by visiting these sites. Tomorrow we are heading to Turkey to meet with friends and colleagues from different countries.

A few days ago, there was an exchange of prisoners of war between Ukraine and Russia, and 215 Ukrainian soldiers were freed. I checked the list of their names but couldn't find my friend, the human rights activist Max Butkevych, among them. I'm happy that many of our fighters were released, but I'm thinking of Max. How is he? Does he know that some have escaped that hell?

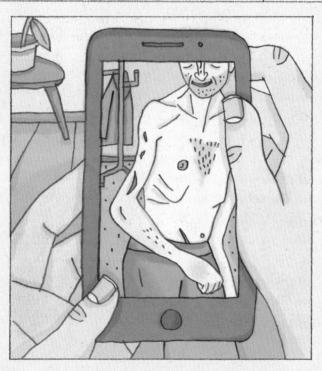

I saw a photo of Mykhailo Dianov, one of the freed Ukrainian soldiers. He looks like he was tortured. There are scars on his face. Before his capture, he had broken his arm during combat. I read that his Russian captors took out the shrapnel with rusty pliers and without anesthesia. The bone did not heal well. Looking at this picture is hard. That's why social media platforms try to hide such photos from the public. But to understand what's going on, we need to look at such images. They remind us that we're all humans, and that people should never do such things to one another.

The military draft began, and I panicked a little when I heard this news. As someone with no military background, I'm not the first in line, but the government lies all the time, so you never know. I have to be honest: I decided not to join the antimobilization demonstrations. I'm afraid of the police violence.

Sad news: I was able to get a bus ticket, and I left Russia last Friday. My family is back in St. Petersburg. I'm now in Helsinki. At first, I was nervous. But when I got on the bus, I started feeling better. I saw more than seventy cars at the border to Finland. I spent two and a half hours on the Russian side, waiting to get out. The border guards inspected everybody's luggage and asked some

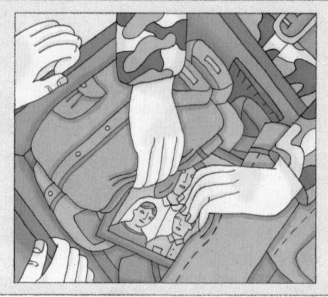

of us to open our suitcases. There were a lot of young men. I'm sure that most of them were there for the same reason I was: to flee from the draft. I could sense that everyone around me was stressed. None of us spoke. In the end, everyone on the bus was able to enter Finland. I feel like I've escaped. It looks like Putin will ban men from leaving Russia this week. Then the only options will be to fight in the war, to resist Putin or to hide in the forest.

I have only a few weeks left to remain in the EU on my current visa. I'm flying to Istanbul on Thursday, where I can stay without a visa for a while with friends who immigrated there last spring. Poland and the Baltics closed their borders to Russian tourists last week, and Finland might do the same soon. I must find a way of getting an EU residence permit. I have to to calm down. Then I'll make a decision.

I've been thinking a lot about the trauma caused by this war. I feel that I'm stuck in Limbo. A lot of good things are happening to me, but I don't feel happy. It's as if I've just given birth to a child and I know that I'm supposed to feel incredible, but the baby is constantly crying, and all that remains is a great sense of fatigue.

I was in Turkey last week and saw many Russians who, I assumed, came there because of the draft. There were many strong-looking men of conscription age staying at the same hotel where I was staying. Seeing them made me feel scared. I worried that some would decide to attack me or my friends if they found out that we are Ukrainian. I avoided any personal interaction with them, and even the hotel staff seemed to try to separate us from each other.

They sat Ukrainian guests in one part of the restaurant, and Russian guests in another. I overheard some of the Russians' conversations and heard them talking about the draft. We decided to only speak in Ukrainian, not in Russian, because we didn't want them to understand what we were talking about. When they heard us speak Ukrainian, they looked at us with an expression of frustration, or even fear, on their faces.

Then I saw hundreds of Russians at the airport. There were many families, and I felt badly for their kids: What kind of life do they have now? If their parents support Putin and the genocide against the Ukrainians, then they will grow up hating Ukraine and the West. Still, I'm hopeful that those kids will grow up to be different than their parents, and that they will feel compelled to change something.

I'm in Istanbul, and I feel disoriented. No one needs me here. I have no social status. I live in a state of total uncertainty. I smoke a lot. I'm staying in Kadıköy, and all I can say is that it's big and noisy, and that there are a lot of people. I'm not used to being among this many people. My friends here are helping me settle in. There are a lot of Russians here. Today I bumped into someone in the street whom I know from St. Petersburg. My friends tell me that this happens to them regularly. I spend my days walking around the neighborhood and going to cafés with my friends, where I drink a lot of tea. I also went to IKEA to buy towels. Going there felt very familiar because I saw some of the furniture I have in my apartment in St. Petersburg, which I bought before IKEA closed down in Russia.

My wife is relieved that I was able to leave Russia. We decided not to tell our kids that I left because of the draft. We told them instead that I was going back to Riga for work — for one because we didn't want to scare them, but also because we're worried they could accidentally mention it at school.

I don't know when I'll ever be able to return to my home country, and I still can't believe that this is my new reality. I don't know yet if I want to stay here or go elsewhere. I need time to understand what I want. I've been helping my friends clean their apartment. I mop the floor and wash the dishes. It allows me to feel like I'm living a real life.

I was in New York for a conference last week — my first time in the U.S.! Going back and forth between a war zone and countries where life functions normally isn't a conflict for me. I need to experience normal life. Several people in New York told me that they're worried about a civil war breaking out in the U.S. because of how divided their society is. That sounds unlikely to me because I think that there are enough people in the U.S. who would prevent a war from happening.

When I arrived back in Denmark, I read the horrible news: Putin has bombed cities across Ukraine in retaliation for the recent explosion at the Crimean Bridge. My father-in-law is still in Kyiv because he's not yet sixty, and men between eighteen and sixty years of age are still not allowed to leave Ukraine. He told me that he saw rockets flying above his head. At a supermarket, he saw a woman who screamed out: "We will all die here!" Then she lost consciousness.

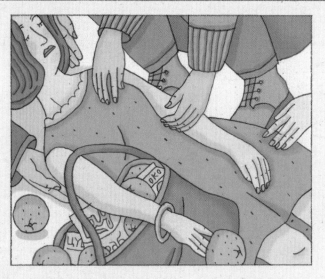

A lot of people in Ukraine have gone crazy because of all that's happened. I don't go on Facebook much anymore because of all the hate speech; I only use it to check where my friends are, or if they're still alive. I don't see an immediate future for my family in Ukraine. Cultural institutions in Kyiv have shut down. It's important to me that my kids grow up in a cultural environment. When I go back to Ukraine, I go straight to the frontline of the fighting to report, because all the people who are important to me have left Kyiv and won't return in the near future.

Last week went by very quickly. I continue helping my friends in Istanbul with their household chores. I cook food, wash dishes, pick up their daughter from school. Just like before, I begin every day by reading the news. After the explosion at the Crimean Bridge, I started worrying about Russia's response. And then it happened: the massive bombing of Ukraine. One shell even hit a playground. Yesterday was unbearably hard, and it was difficult for me to do anything. Only in the evening, when gathering with my friends, was I able to relax a bit. I often think about how I can help with the rebuilding of Ukraine. I don't have great financial resources, but I'm making sure to reserve a portion of my monthly budget for donations. These payments will be small, but regular.

No matter what happens, I think that Russia has already lost. Its economy has visibly declined and will decline further. Its society is divided between those who support the war and those who don't. It's hard for me to make predictions for Russia's future. A federal system that allows individual regions to make their own decisions independently from Moscow would be better. It's impossible to imagine my future in Russia when I can't even understand my life in the present. I hope that, eventually, I'll be able to engage in the same activities as before the war, and to share my experience with others. But I don't know if I'll be a very social person at that point. For the moment, I have a desire for privacy — I feel like hiding in a cabin in the forest.

I'm tired. The past months were so intense that the only thing I'm wishing for right now is sleep. Even after waking up, I feel as if I'm still asleep. I think my body is trying to tell me that I must slow down and take care of myself. But I can't. I'm constantly thinking of the war, of my family, of my friends — and of my enemies. The war seems to have no ending. There is no space for me to think. Before the invasion, in my apartment in Ukraine, I was able to spend time alone, to think and read or write. While in New York, I bought some great books that I brought back with me to Denmark, but I haven't had time to read them. This makes me sad because I love to read so much.

Russia recently started using Iranian Shahed drones to attack Ukraine. They really scare me. These drones are simple and stupid, but unpredictable, and it's very hard to shoot them down. They targeted our power plants and have destroyed 30% of our electrical system. More than a thousand towns and villages now are without power, which also means that many people don't have water. And it will get even worse from here on because Russia wants to destroy our entire country. It feels like the apocalypse. Tomorrow, I'll return to Ukraine to report on the war from there.

People here in Istanbul don't seem to have a problem with the fact that I am Russian. Sometimes I meet immigrants from other former Soviet countries, chefs or waiters at the restaurants where I eat, and they seem to take pleasure in meeting me, and in speaking Russian. I haven't seen any Ukrainian flags in Istanbul. The only visual evidence pointing to the war is the large numbers of Russians in the streets. They look frightened — I can see fear in their eyes. When I notice men in the street who look like that, I play a little game: I speculate that they are Russians, and when I walk past them, I listen to their conversations to find out.

I read some articles about Turkish history. I visited the Basilica Cistern, a giant, nearly 1,500-year-old water reservoir. Standing next to it, I suddenly felt small. There were many tourists visiting the site, and I thought: "I am neither a tourist, nor a resident of Istanbul. I'm not even a real immigrant."

I don't know who I am. When my wife buys groceries in St. Petersburg, I receive a digital receipt in my inbox. Each time I see it, I remember the times when I went shopping there. Now that I'm gone, my wife is realizing how much I used to do for our family. Adding new chores to her routine is hard for her, but she's great and she gets it all done. I used to take charge of the shopping and the cooking, used to wake up the kids, bring them to school in the morning and to bed at night.

I miss my easy and predictable routine. I miss sights and places familiar to my eyes. I haven't found such places here. My main place in Istanbul is the bench in front of the house where I now live.

I'm back in Ukraine. These days, when I speak with someone about making plans for the future, I use the expression "if we survive." That's how I feel. I hope that most Ukrainians will survive.

A few days ago, I was at the house with the woodburning stove in Lviv, which we recently started renting. It's big and warm. We have a small backyard with trees and grapevines. I was talking to my colleagues via Zoom when I suddenly heard a weird sound. At first, I thought it was an Iranian combat drone, and I was pretty scared. I looked out the window and saw a Ukrainian fighter jet just passing above our house. My husband later told me that our house is near an air base, and that this happens all the time.

Now I'm at my old apartment in Kyiv, and it feels like a stage set. Before the invasion, I spent time here with my kids. They're not here anymore. The rooms feel dead. The apartment is like an empty box. It doesn't feel like home; it doesn't feel like my life. A few days ago, my husband, who is with me, asked if I'd be ready to leave our apartment, to give it up for good. I walked into the children's room and remembered how my older son played there, how he played with my younger son, how we read fairy tales together. I broke out in tears. My husband saw that I was crying and told me that we don't need to leave immediately, that there's time. The apartment feels like a haunted house from the past. It exists merely as a collection of memories. It's painful.

I received an invitation from a French cultural institute that I've worked with in the past and that might be able to act as a sponsor for my residence permit to France. If it works out, I'll need to find an apartment and figure out how to make a living and build a new life in Paris. I imagined what would happen if the French police were to confront me with questions at the border. I started reasoning with them in French in my mind, explaining my situation and telling them about my involvement with the French art scene. But then, last Thursday, I flew to Paris from Istanbul, and no questions were asked at the border at all. A French man at the airport even bought me a tram ticket because my Russian bank card is blocked abroad and I didn't have the right amount of change.

Paris is a beautiful city. I was here with my wife five years ago, and I've been trying to find the sites that we visited together. I spent some time with a friend from St. Petersburg who immigrated here. Going for a walk, and then sitting by the Seine with her, drinking wine and eating cheese, really helped me. We spoke about the way things used to be, and about our current situations.

I'm staying with a French friend. He's an artist too. Today I met his cleaning lady. She's from Moldavia, and my friend told me she speaks Russian. We talked about the war, and she told me that her sister lives in Russia and doesn't want to leave. I didn't ask if her sister is in favor of or against the war. I don't think it is ethical for me to ask. I don't want to hurt her feelings. And in any case, it's I — not her and her sister — who's from the country of the perpetrators.

I'm in Lviv where I've been hearing explosions, but at least we have electricity and running water. I spent a few days in Kyiv, and it wasn't easy due to the blackouts. Our electric power plants were hit by Iranian drones, so, to conserve energy, electricity is switched off in some regions for up to twelve hours a day. This means that people in some multistory apartment buildings are experiencing water shortages. It's not yet cold outside so there's no need for heat. But winter is coming soon, and it will be tough.

Areas across Ukraine have issued schedules listing the dates and times during which their power is switched off. I was told by the electric company that our building in Kyiv has complicated wiring that makes it impossible to determine the exact times of the blackouts. I planned to do some work and to prepare breakfast during the times when no blackouts were scheduled, but suddenly the electricity went off and I had to leave my apartment to get breakfast at the nearest café. One night I came home and realized that there was no electricity in our building. I had to walk up twenty floors and sat in the dark in my apartment for hours till they turned the lights back on. My husband and I were joking that if you want to make the Ukrainian energy company laugh, you just have to tell them your plans for the day. This week, we're hosting a workshop that will teach journalists in Ukraine how to survive bombings and help wounded civilians. Teaching this workshop will be a challenge because of the blackouts and drones.

During the first few days in Paris, I had trouble falling asleep. Maybe it's because I read the news in bed. When I can't sleep, I imagine my family close by, and eventually I will fall asleep. I've been meeting with French publishers to see if I can work for them. The cost of living in France is higher than in Russia, so I'm not sure I can continue working as an artist here. I saw my Russian friend again. This time, we didn't speak about the war, and everything felt all right. I also met with some of my fellow artist friends in St. Petersburg on Zoom. We spoke about our work. Working hard helps us navigate our current lives. My art is a kind of anchor for me.

A few days ago, I went to a party at a cultural space called Agency of Artists in Exile. It's an organization that supports artists from all over the world, including Russians. The party opened with a concert by a rap musician from the Ural region. There was a Ukrainian woman there, who's been living in France for 3 years. We spoke in Russian — but not about the war, only about simple things.

My kids called me a few days ago, to ask for help with their homework — and to check if I knew the answers. They told me about their new computer games and comic books, and about what they want for their birthdays. I explained that I don't know if I'll be back in time. I still haven't told them that we're planning to emigrate as a family. It's become increasingly difficult for my wife to speak about our emigration when we don't have a real plan for it yet. Not being able to talk to her about it is difficult for me. I have to prepare everything by myself in Paris, and once I have it all figured out, she will pack the suitcases.

My husband and I are back in Kyiv. I spent three days training in tactical medicine, so I could learn how to save lives at the frontline. Tomorrow I'll go to Irpin and Bucha just outside of Kyiv, to find out how people there cope with the trauma they've experienced since the invasion, and how they are preparing for the winter.

Temperatures have been dropping to freezing at night. We have heat in our apartment only when the electricity is on. I wear woolen clothes and plush slippers. We now have an average of twelve hours of blackouts a day: four hours in the morning, four in the afternoon and four during the night. Our daily activities follow the energy company's schedule. It determines when we prepare breakfast, when we need to go out to find a café with electricity where we can work, and when to return home, after the power is back on. Yesterday we spent an hour in our car, waiting for the electricity to come back on in our building because it's very hard to walk up the twenty flights to our apartment when the elevator isn't working.

When people ask me if I've "returned" to Kyiv, I don't know what to say because I don't feel like I'm returning anywhere. This is how I live now: I move back and forth between two realities, Copenhagen and Kyiv. And it doesn't even feel like a problem to me anymore. Not staying in one place for too long feels like a system. At least I have a system. People who live in post-Soviet countries usually say that temporary things are the only things that are permanent. That's what I'm experiencing now.

This week I moved to the Cité internationale des arts, an artist residency in Paris that's supported by the Institut français. I was told that there are quite a few other Russians at the Cité who've escaped the draft, and who are receiving support. I have a studio here until the end of December, and a grant that helps me financially for two months, so I am OK for now. I visited the city of Arles, to meet with a publisher. He invited me and my family to come and stay at his house. Sharing a house when you are young and single is one thing. But sharing a kitchen and bathroom between two families makes it difficult to maintain a sense of privacy. From now on, I need to get used to living alone.

Two days ago, I got my Pfizer COVID vaccine in Paris. Before that I only had the Russian Sputnik V vaccine, but that one isn't accepted here. The World Health Organization postponed the evaluation of the vaccine indefinitely last spring because of Russia's invasion of Ukraine.

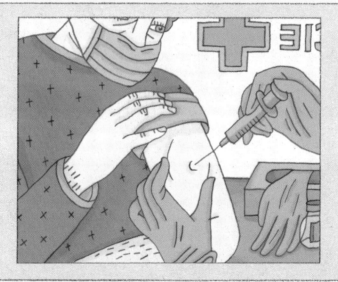

I've been thinking about the idea of guilt. As a Russian, I feel guilty. At the same time, I'm against the idea of collective guilt because I think that collective guilt stops you from confronting your personal guilt. Do I feel personal guilt? I don't know. I worked hard over the years to try to change my country by exposing it to the international art world, and to the artists I invited to come to Russia. I understand now that that wasn't enough. But while I know that this work didn't really change anything, I still hope that it reached some individuals. I don't think I could have done more than I did.

Tomorrow morning I'll go to Kherson to report. I'm so happy about Kherson's liberation. People there suffered under the occupation for almost nine months. Now they are free. But there is still no water or electricity, so people live a difficult life. The father of a friend of mine, who lives in Kherson, was captured and tortured with electroshocks by the Russians because he refused to collaborate with them. They finally threw him out on the street, and he returned home just a few weeks ago. He barely survived. My friend was able to reunite with him and sent me a photo of the two of them celebrating the liberation of Kherson together.

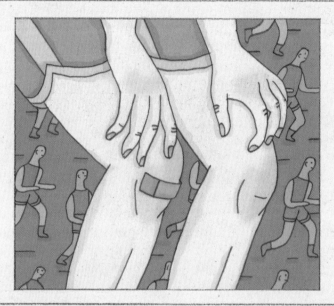

Sometimes I feel like I'm running a marathon: I've already used up all my reserves, but when I stop to take a break, my trainer tells me to continue running, without interruption, for another thousand kilometers. I don't have any more energy, but I also don't have the option of putting the war on hold and relaxing.

I haven't seen my children for almost a month, and I still won't see them for another few weeks. I caught myself thinking that it's better for me not to be with my kids at all because when I work on my reporting, I constantly have to deal with difficult situations, and I am nervous. When they are with me, I feel even more vulnerable and anxious. And I can't share this anxiety with them because it would be unfair to them. Admitting to these feelings makes me sad. I don't think I'm a very good mother.

The language is the only problem for me here in Paris. People tell me that my French is good, but when I speak it, I have to concentrate, and I get tired. It was easier in Riga where I was mostly able to speak Russian. I visited the Musée de l'Orangerie. It was great to see paintings by Matisse, Picasso and Monet. A Russian friend once said to me: "If you find yourself in a strange situation, go to the museum." Over the past six months, I've visited museums in Riga, Vilnius, Istanbul and now Paris. Art disconnects you from reality — at least for a while.

I haven't been able to open a French bank account. Even with a residence permit, banks block Russians from opening accounts. I brought some cash from Russia that I'm living off of, and I opened an account on my phone in the name of a Finnish friend. I'm hoping that, once I have my residence permit, I'll find an online bank that will allow me to open an account in my own name.

I had a bad dream: My wife told me that she'd decided to stay in Russia with the children because there is no certainty for us in France. At first, I didn't want to tell her about the dream. But when I finally did, she told me that this wasn't true and that I shouldn't be afraid. It was her birthday last week. I asked a friend of mine in St. Petersburg to drop off a gift and flowers at our apartment from me. In the evening, I had dinner with friends in Paris, and I brought a cake to celebrate her birthday. We called her and sang a birthday song for her in French. That was the most important thing that happened last week.

I went to liberated Kherson last week. Many of my journalist friends are from that city, but couldn't return while it was under Russian occupation. They were incredibly happy to be back. What would be the first thing I'd do if I returned to liberated Crimea, the place where I spent so many years of my life? Would I kneel down and kiss the soil? That's not really my kind of thing. But I miss Crimea so much that I think I'd go crazy with happiness if I returned there. Kherson is grim. There is no electricity, no heating, no water and almost no cellphone connection. Thousands of locals gather every day in the main square to get food and water distributed by humanitarian aid organizations. Some share their food with those who can't wait in line. Many stores are closed because of the constant blackouts. Food production has slowed down because there is no electricity. And yet, people continue to celebrate the liberation. It's powerful to see.

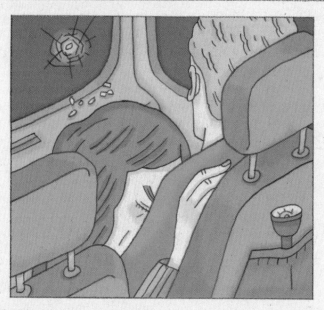

People shared stories with me about how they hid from the Russian soldiers in their homes, and some talked about being interrogated by the Russians. Many people were tortured. One woman told me that her husband was killed one night while they were driving home with their young son, just ten minutes after the curfew began. A sniper shot him in the head. Her friend's uncle was also killed by a sniper while walking to work one morning right before the curfew ended. How can a human being do such a thing?

I went to La MEP museum in Paris for an exhibition by the Ukrainian photographer Boris Mikhailov. There were a lot of photos from the time of the Soviet regime. The series about his hometown of Kharkov reminded me very much of the towns I saw growing up in Russia. Seeing people marching with red flags made me think of the parades I took part in as a child. I remembered how happy I was at those moments, and I suddenly felt nostalgic. There were also photos from the years right after the Soviet collapse. Those were harder to look at because they reminded me of what my hometown looked like at the time: dirty streets littered with drunkards, slogans smeared on the walls.

Looking at these photos, I thought that one thing that Ukrainians and Russians share is the trauma of the post-Soviet era. Russia hasn't been able to overcome this trauma. When the sanctions were imposed at the beginning of the war, many Russians said that we'll survive them the same way we survived the difficult economic situation of the post-Soviet era. People seem not to be able to let go of that time, and readily apply that experience to what is going on today. Ukraine, on the other hand, seems to have been able to move on. When visiting Ukraine in the past, I found people there to be more open-minded, and I felt a stronger sense of freedom there. During Soviet times, my mother worked with a lot of Ukrainians. She told me that she was very moved by how Ukrainian men talked about their wives, praising them in the highest terms. She said that Russian men never praised their wives that way.

Крымъ.   ЯЛТА,

Fall – Winter

I returned from Kherson to a dark and cold Kyiv. Getting up to my apartment on the twentieth floor without a working elevator during the blackouts has become too difficult, so I stayed with my husband's parents who live on the first floor in a different building. They have a different kind of electrical system, and there is heat and warm water even during the blackouts, which feels surreal to me. I had a hot dinner (much different from the dried food rations I ate all week in Kherson), and I took a warm bath — the gold standard!

I interviewed Ukrainians who were tortured in Kherson during the Russian occupation. I've noticed that people don't usually cry when they tell me about the horrible things that they've experienced. But when they talk about how what happened to them affected their family members emotionally, they suddenly start sobbing. The pain of their loved ones seems harder for them to bear than their own pain. Maybe there is a historic reason — during Soviet times, people were told not to show their true emotions, but to appear rational and steely. Or maybe it's just a kind of coping mechanism.

After Kyiv, I visited Lviv. Then Russia started shelling power plants again, and I found myself in the outskirts of town without electricity or heating, and with no cellphone connection. One day, I had to go into town but couldn't order a taxi because my internet connection didn't work. I actually had to call my husband in Denmark, so he could order a taxi for me. It sounds like a joke — but that's the reality that Russia is forcing us to live in. Today, my husband left Copenhagen for Ukraine again. The kids didn't want him to leave. It's sad.

Yesterday was Mother's Day in Russia. I called my mother and we spoke about the weather. Usually, we don't talk about my immigration or the war because it gets her down. But yesterday she told me that my leaving Russia was a good idea. My brother recently imigrated to Belgrade and it's hard for her because she doesn't know when she'll see her sons again. "If the war continues for much longer," she said, "then everyone in Russia will go crazy. Many won't survive this nightmare." Still, I don't think that she would emigrate with us. At one point in her life, she had considered moving to another country. She regrets now that she never did. At this point, it's too late. She lives alone and doesn't have the strength. She divorced my father when I was eight. My father is pro-Putin. We stopped being close a long time ago.

My mother told me about posters that have appeared recently in the entrance area of her building: infographics that tell residents what to do and where to go in case of a bomb attack. Russia is now on what they call a special readiness alert level. I try not to think about the possibility of a bombing. Previously, my hometown's local government had told residents that there aren't any shelters in the city and that, in the case of a bombing, everything would be destroyed anyway because of the town's industrial infrastructure. Now they are distributing these posters with addresses of nearby shelters — yet more proof that they are lying, my mother said. She sent me a picture of the poster. The same kind of poster designed during Soviet times would look so much better.

Back in Copenhagen, I wake up in my apartment, with everything a human being needs: light, heat and clean water. What joy it is to have access to these basic human inventions, after living without them for weeks while reporting from Ukraine! But how sad to think that millions of Ukrainians don't have those things right now. Many stay in freezing apartments, unable to cook proper food, while also living in fear of Russian bombs. I'm beginning to understand the massive impact that weather has on humans.

Everybody in Ukraine is discussing the weather now. Men between the ages of eighteen and sixty are still not allowed to leave the country, and some simply don't have the resources to leave. What will happen to them during the cold winter months? You might argue that supporting repair initiatives while the war continues is a waste of money because Russia could destroy everything all over again. But repair is crucial. You can't live in a house without a roof in the winter. A few months ago, I went to Bucha to interview its mayor. The mayor told me that all of the Western politicians who came to express their loyalty told him that they will only financially support the reconstruction once the war is over. Most of the reconstruction money is coming from the Ukrainian government and local communities. And it's next to nothing.

A few days ago, it was my husband's birthday. Living through the war is much easier knowing that I have him in my life.

Last week, I went to a concert in Paris. While waiting in line for the restroom, I told the French woman standing next to me that I'd seen this band perform once before. She asked me where. When I told her in St. Petersburg, she said: "So, you are Russian?" "Yes," I said, to which she replied, "I'm sorry." She didn't mean it ironically. She sounded empathetic. Being asked where I am from is the most difficult question to answer these days. But in a small way, I felt supported by her.

I went to see a performance at Les Halles shopping center that was written by a group of Ukrainian artists and produced by my Russian friend who immigrated to Paris. The audience was given headphones and asked whether they wanted to listen in Ukrainian or French. I chose Ukrainian — I only understood half of what was said, but listening in Ukrainian made me feel connected. The play began with the sound of an air raid siren, after which the audience was asked to go down to the basement floor of the shopping center, as if walking down to a bomb shelter. This immediately plunged me into the reality of the war. Then the headphones played a series of stories based on everyday experiences of Ukrainians. One by one, Ukrainians shared their feelings about the war. At the beginning, I felt an impulse to take off my headphones — it was hard to hear those stories. From time to time there were tears in my eyes. But I forced myself to listen. What was also difficult was seeing all the other people at the shopping center who were listening in Ukrainian. I was afraid to look them in the eyes.

I've had the flu for more than a week now, so I'm exhausted. But I feel good mentally. Having everything I need for my daily life makes me feel so much better than how I felt in Ukraine, where I lacked the most basic things for two months. I expect to stay in Copenhagen with the kids until the end of the year. I've started learning Danish, mostly to support my sons who also have to learn it, but also because I think it will help us integrate. My older son's Danish isn't very good yet, but he is a quick learner. The other week, he came home and sang a Danish song that he had learned at school. It seems to me that people in Denmark sing a lot. This feels strange to me because Ukrainians don't usually sing together, except when it's our national anthem.

I was invited to a Christmas party at my Danish friend's place, and all the guests were singing the entire time! I only know one Danish song. I recently took an ancestry test and found out that a small part of me is Inuit! Now that I know this is my genetic heritage, I've become even more interested in learning about Danish culture.

I found out that my Twitter account has been "ghost banned." This means that many of my followers aren't seeing my posts any longer. Twitter is also canceling the newsletter platform I've been using, so my reports from the frontline will soon be shut down. I will lose the monthly subscription fees that I've been collecting to support my journalist colleagues. The same thing is happening to many other Ukrainian journalists. Elon Musk is an opportunist who uses his influence to gain more power. It's disgusting.

I got my second COVID shot, and I'm feeling sick. Paris is looking very smart with its Christmas and New Year's decorations. There are a lot of people in the streets, smiling and taking pictures. I've tried to get into the holiday spirit, but it isn't really working. I'm still waiting for my residency permit. In the meantime, my visa has run out, so I'm now officially illegal in France. I considered going to Russia for New Year's. But if I leave now, I might be barred from reentering France for years to come because I've overstayed my visa.

On New Year's Eve, my family usually prepares an elaborate meal. We watch movies, and after midnight, go for a walk in the neighborhood. Everyone gets a gift. The kids can't open theirs before the morning. If they opened them on New Year's Eve, they'd end up playing with them all night. This year, I sent gifts by mail: Lego sets and Nintendo games for the kids, and warm pajamas for my wife.

I talked to the children yesterday and informed them that I won't come home for New Year's. They asked if I'd come for my younger child's birthday on February 1st, but I said I didn't know. I explained, for the first time, why I really left Russia. My younger kid agreed that leaving was better than going to war. My older one just said, "Ah! I understand," and proceeded to tell me about a new computer game. We used to go for walks together and talk about those games. I miss those walks a lot. My younger one asked if we could meet in Riga in the summer. Seeing my kid's disappointed face when I said that we might not meet before then was very hard. I'm actually crying as I'm writing this. It's only the second or third time that I've cried since the beginning of the war.

I'm still sick with the flu, and it's driving me crazy. I've been sick since I left Ukraine two weeks ago. I'm wondering if it's my body's response to feeling more relaxed now that I'm in Copenhagen.

It was my birthday last week. Thinking about the past year, I realize that I am lucky: I'm alive; I am doing the kind of work I love to do; I am surrounded by wonderful, supportive people; I have the best family, the best partner I could have wished for. Despite the frightening situation I find myself in, I have everything I need. My Ukrainian friend came from Berlin to celebrate with me, and it was exactly what I needed. Before the war, I used to celebrate my birthday with dozens of people at nice places in Kyiv. Thanks to Russia, I can't do that anymore. Instead my friend and I spent the day walking the streets of Copenhagen, going to museums and talking about our lives, problems and hopes.

Russia doesn't only bring destruction — it also affects our friendships. I lost many friends in Crimea, where I used to live, since its annexation in 2014. I haven't returned to Crimea since because Russia blacklisted me for my work as a journalist. Just a few friends from there have stayed in touch. It's hard to be this far away from them. I've also been thinking about my childhood friends in Russia, where I grew up. I haven't spoken to them in years. Most of them take Putin's side. Some even called me a traitor for supporting Ukraine. I don't have the energy to convince them otherwise.

I'll spend this Christmas with my kids and my mother here in Copenhagen. My husband is in Ukraine. It's sad we can't be together for the holidays.

Today begins my last week of the artist residency in Paris. I have to get my life in order and find a place to live. I had a difficult conversation with my wife. She was under the impression that I've already emotionally adjusted to my new life. For the first time, I told her about all the doubts and fears that I feel: I have no social standing in France; I have no apartment that I could bring my family to; I feel lonely, even though I've met many people here. I had avoided telling her all this because she already has a lot to worry about. It's hard for her to understand my situation. Usually I try to focus on the positive when we talk.

What could a post-war reconciliation between Ukraine and Russia look like? I think it would have to be a cessation of hostility towards Ukraine; Russia's retreat from all Ukrainian territories; and reparations, reparations and more reparations. In order for Russia to change, we would have to replace everyone in government. Putin can have no part in this conversation.
And Russia should apologize. But rather than words, we must apologize through deeds, and participate financially in the rebuilding of Ukraine — but without meddling in Ukraine's affairs. As for social change in Russia — that would take ten years or more.
It will be difficult for people to acknowledge the fact that by supporting Putin, they actually supported a Nazi-like regime.

My husband got special permission to leave Ukraine due to his work as a journalist and was able to join us in Copenhagen for Christmas! We celebrated with my mother and our Danish friend, and it was great. We had a traditional Danish meal and wine, and we exchanged gifts. I never thought that this year's Christmas would be so special, despite all the difficulties. And I realize that the war has changed me. I appreciate my family in a way that I've never appreciated them before. It's easier for me to accept their quirks. The war also made me understand that simple actions can help save lives, and that sharing with others is important because, as humans, we rely on each other's knowledge and support during times of crisis.

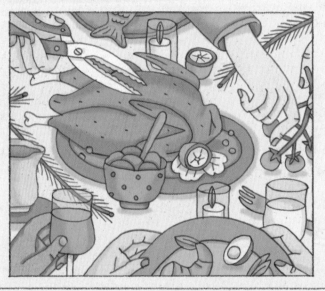

My mother, who is an archeologist and academic, can't find a job in Denmark because she has a Russian passport. She lived as a Russian in Crimea for many years and applied for a Ukrainian passport back in 2014 but didn't get it because of Crimea's annexation. She can't get a Ukrainian passport now, either, because of the war. Danish universities don't want to hire her, so she's planning to return to Crimea. My mom's husband, who grew up there as a Ukrainian, still lives in Crimea, and doesn't want to leave. My mother accepts the fact that this is her only option now, but she is very sad about it. I worry that it could be dangerous for her to return because of the shelling, but also because she has many visas from the European Union in her passport and is openly pro-Ukrainian. I don't even want to think about what could happen to her.

I celebrated Christmas at my artist residency. There were people from various countries, including Australia and Korea. We had mac and cheese and hot wine. I proposed that we listen to Russian music, so we played Monetochka, a popular Russian singer who recently immigrated to Lithuania and has been performing to raise funds for Ukraine. I spoke Russian with a group of Latvian and Armenian artists. One of the things I miss most about Russia is its language. But Russian, to me, represents much more than just my country — it's the feeling that you can easily understand each other.

Later that evening, I went to a party for Russian émigrées. Most of them I had never met before, so I felt a little insecure. At the end of the evening, one of the guests became very emotional — she was a little tipsy. She talked about how paralyzed she feels, and how much she wants Putin to die. I feel that Russians in Paris can speak openly against the war, as long as they're speaking in private.

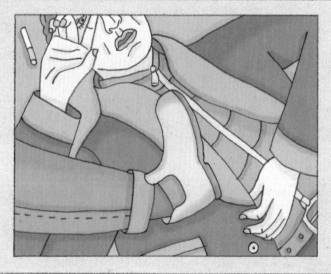

On the way home, I was attacked in the street. A man asked for a cigarette as two others approached me from behind. They pushed me to the ground and beat me up. They spoke to me in French, and at first, I replied in French. But then I started screaming obscene words, and calling for help, in Russian. I thought that speaking in a foreign language might scare them. I pulled thirty Euros from my pocket and gave it to them. I have a black eye now. Up until the attack, I'd been associating my emotional trauma with Paris — I live in a foreign country without a social status.
Now I also have a physical trauma — ha!

On New Year's Eve, I went for a walk with my husband and our sons around a beautiful lake near our apartment in Copenhagen. There were many ducks and seagulls, and a white swan. We fed them cookies, and the swan was eating right from my sons' hands. There was no other swan in sight, which seemed odd, given that swans often mate for life. I noticed that the swan walked slowly and with a limp. I wondered if something bad had happened to its partner, and I felt sad for it: Even for a swan living in a place as beautiful and peaceful as this, there is no absolute happiness.

After returning to the apartment, I tried to make sense of everything that happened last year. I looked at photographs on my phone for reference. There were so many photos of birds — pigeons, ducks and seagulls — that I took at the canal across from my apartment in Kyiv every day last year before the invasion. It seems that my habit of watching and feeding birds is the one thing that has remained the same in my life since the war began.

My husband decided to show my seven-year-old son President Zelensky's New Year's speech. When Zelensky talked about the many victims of the war, the video suddenly featured images of bomb attacks, injured people and blood. My son started crying. We explained to him that what he saw on the screen wasn't happening in real time, and that he doesn't need to worry. He told us that no one should ever have to see such things. I agree with him. It seems that the person who directed the video didn't consider that this would be watched by children, or other traumatized Ukrainians. I really need some rest in 2023 — but I don't know how to get it.

A group of friends from St. Petersburg and I spent New Year's Eve with a French friend in Rennes. We brought a traditional Russian salad with mayonnaise, and it was a great success! When people at the party started dancing, I couldn't get myself to join in the fun. I thought about my family all night. Christmas isn't that important for us because we aren't religious; New Year's Eve is a more important holiday, and this was the first time we weren't together as a family for it. Some of the party guests came with their children. It was difficult for me to look at them. Seeing them made me think of my own children, and about how sad they are that we can't celebrate together. When it was midnight in St. Petersburg, I called my family, and we wished each other a happy new year.

A lot of Russians have just one hope for the new year: that Vladimir Putin dies. Many of my friends have alluded to this on their social media sites, but without directly mentioning his name. Even though it feels bad to wish death upon anyone, it is something I think about as well. But my biggest dream is to see my family again. I'm still waiting for my residence permit, so I'm stuck in France for the time being. I feel like nothing is in my control. I am trying to get involved in an art project that is planned for this fall in Arles. If it works out, I'll try to find an apartment in Arles for my family. Some weeks ago, my wife asked my children if they could imagine coming to France to see me. They said that they could, but just for a vacation, because our apartment in St. Petersburg is where they really want to live.

I began working as a journalist at the age of 16. Working in this field has given me more wrinkles and health issues than I had expected, but it also gave me a better understanding of what the world is made of. I often say that "I know too much" — journalists see worse things than most other people. It affects my life. But as a journalist, it's my duty to collect the evidence needed for the world to understand why dictators must be overthrown.

Sometimes I want to reveal the truth so badly that I end up in dangerous situations. In 2014, I interviewed Igor Bezler, the then pro-Russian rebel leader in charge of the occupied Donbas region. His nickname was Bes, meaning "devil." I went to his operational base, and I knew that he kept Ukrainian activists as prisoners in the basement. He told me to leave my phone outside the interview room, but I secretly smuggled in a second one. He gave me permission to go down to the basement, where I met some of his prisoners. During my visit, Bes told me to "be careful, otherwise you might die." (I later found out that he had previously tortured another female journalist for saying something he didn't like.) Not long after, my colleagues and I were able to help with the release of the prisoners. Now, I think a lot more about my safety as a journalist because I am a mother. Motherhood has made me wiser.

I wish I could still report from the occupied regions, but I can't because, as a Ukrainian journalist, I am banned from there. I don't feel as useful as I was in 2014.

I spent the beginning of the year going on small trips with my friends along the northern coastline of France. In Saint-Malo we visited a small beach. As we sat by the sea, we saw the high tide coming in. An hour later, the water had covered the entire beach. It occurred to me that the same thing is currently happening in Russia: my country is being washed away, cleansed by a massive tide. After the high tide, the low tide will return.

Even though I'm outside of Russia, I'm afraid of speaking out against the war in public. I worry that my family in Russia will get in trouble if I do. I was at a children's book fair in Paris recently. During an award ceremony, I was asked to join others on a stage to talk about my work. I declined because I was worried I'd have to share my opinions on the war in public on that stage.

Recently, I began wondering whether I might get into trouble for my work, some of which focuses on LGBT issues. Last year, Russia passed a law that bans what it describes as "LGBT propaganda." I don't know if my work falls into that category because there are no specific rules to this law, and no one knows exactly what it means.

I used to collaborate with a friend, a Russian artist who made a book about her family's experience resisting the Soviet regime. Some of her Russian friends died as soldiers during the Russian occupation of the Donbas region eight years ago. She supported them, and she's also been in favor of the current war. I wrote to her recently to let her know that I can no longer work with her, and I received a short reply: "I'm glad we talked about everything, and that nothing was left unsaid."

Last week, I was shocked by the news of a friend's husband's death. He was a videographer and film editor. After the invasion began, he decided to join the Ukrainian army. He was shot dead in Donbas in December. When his wife wrote about his death on social media, I couldn't believe it. "Not him!" I thought. "Not this family!" He was such a kind, creative and beautiful person. They have a nine-year-old daughter, and they were so good together as a family. The first couple of nights after his death I couldn't sleep, and I felt sick. In my mind, I projected this death onto my own family. I worried about what it would feel like if he had been my husband, if it had been me crying over his body at the morgue. It was so painful to see photos of my friend at her husband's funeral. After this happened, I didn't want to let my husband, who's been with us in Copenhagen, go back to Ukraine. I felt sick when he told me he had bought his return ticket. But life is life, and war is war. There are some things that people just have to get used to.

Back in Ukraine, my husband packed up our Kyiv apartment. It has become useless to us — it's inaccessible during the blackouts and vulnerable to rockets that can destroy it within seconds. I'm glad that I wasn't there for the packing. I think I would have just sat there, in the empty rooms once so familiar to me, and cried. My husband told me that all of our belongings — our beds and shelves, our books, our coffee machine, the art that once hung on our walls — that all of this fit into a 7-cubic-meter-sized van. Now I know that our life measures 7 cubic meters.

I'm worried about my younger kid, who has a severe case of the flu right now. My wife is very tired. She told me that many pharmacies don't carry fever-reducing medicines anymore because of the sanctions. After visiting several shops, she finally found what she needed. The other sanction-related problem for her is dog food. There is less choice and it's more expensive than before.

"Where have you been the last eight years?" This is a propaganda phrase you hear often from pro-war Russians these days. They claim that the war didn't start last year, but in 2014 in Donbas, where a "genocide against Russians" has been taking place ever since. This is used as a justification for Russia's military aggression.

I can't stop reading the news about the war. On Sunday, a Russian bomb destroyed an apartment complex in Dnipro. A lot of people were killed — just another crime committed by the Russian army. When I saw pictures of the building, it reminded me of the way that a lot of Russian buildings look, and I remembered the times that I have spent inside such apartments. This made the tragedy feel even more relatable. In response to the attack and in solidarity with the Ukrainian people, some residents in Moscow laid down flowers at the monument to the Ukrainian poet Lesya Ukrainka. One person put a photo of the bombed-out building on the ground. Two people were arrested for laying down flowers, and another two just for standing nearby.

After 24 hours on the road, I arrived in Kyiv by train. At the station's exit, I was met by border police. When the policewoman looked at my passport, she asked when I had last visited the Russian-occupied territories. I told her that I was there in 2014 to report, but that I can't return there any longer because I'm well-known — and unwanted — as a journalist in Russia. My answer seemed to frustrate her, and she sent a text message to the border security staff. When she got a message back saying that all was clear, I was able to leave the station. Ukrainians seem to have forgotten that people used to travel freely to and from the occupied areas, without being seen as spies or traitors. Ukrainian politicians have created an image of even ordinary people visiting those areas as suspicious. It feeds into their narrative of "divide and conquer."

I'm sure that there are a lot of secret agents amongst the many Russians who have recently immigrated to countries that still welcome them. In Germany, suspected Russian spies organize pro-Russian rallies. It's very worrying. There is an old joke from the 2014 Euromaidan uprising: "If it looks like a horse, sounds like a horse and acts like a horse, it's most likely a horse. And if it says that it's not a horse, then it's definitely a Russian horse." I worry that these undercover agents are spying on Ukrainian activists and journalists in the EU. Ramzan Kadyrov, the Head of the Chechen Republic, recently said that people engaging in anti-Russian protests abroad will be "executed" by pro-Russian operatives. I myself haven't been approached by Russian spies yet, so, for now, everything seems fine.

I feel like the protagonist in the film "Groundhog Day," who is experiencing the same day over and over again: I wake up, realize where I am, read the news, and then there's only pain. I try to work — to get at least a few simple things done to distract myself from my situation. At some point during the day, a feeling of great anxiety sets in, and I go for a walk around the city.
The next day, the same thing happens all over again.

Last week, I received a 6-month residence permit. I plan to apply for a 4-year foreign artist work visa next. I've moved out of the artist residence and am now staying with French friends. They have a large apartment, but also a large family. I already feel that I've been occupying their space for too long, and I need to look for a space of my own soon. At the same time, I worry that renting my own apartment will make me feel even further removed from my wife and children in Russia. I am afraid of losing touch with them. We speak on the phone every day, but we haven't talked about their emigration plans because it would be too emotionally draining when nothing is in place yet to actually move here. We haven't seen each other, hugged each other, in four months. I worry that one day we'll end up living separate lives.

I spent the week in bed with a high fever at my in-law's apartment in Kyiv. I got ill with salmonella after eating at one of Kyiv's best cafés, and it was awful. I've never felt this bad before. Everything hurt. I even stopped smoking! Luckily, there were practically no blackouts, and Russia only attacked Kyiv once. When you're sick and in a warzone, you try to avoid going to the hospital at all costs because you know it's already filled with people who are in a much more critical condition than you.

I have too many things to do, and the stress is affecting me. My therapist tells me that to maintain my sanity I must slow down. But the war drives me to work harder and harder. Like Alice in Wonderland, I must run as fast as I can just to stay in place.

This week, I had several dreams about returning to Crimea. In my dreams, I saw my old friends and visited the Black Sea, and the beach resort towns of Yalta and Koktebel. It's been nine years since I moved away from Crimea, and I didn't expect that I would still miss it so much. In my mind, I constantly travel back in time. It feels as if my real self — my happy self — continues to live in Crimea, while my other life is unfolding here, in the midst of the war, the suffering, the nightmares. Just like my older son, who dreams of returning to Kyiv, of being with his old friends and of the adventures they experienced together there, I dream of a past life that doesn't exist anymore. I know I should let go of it, but I can't because this is exactly what the war is about: We want our country and our past returned to us.

Last week, I attended a festival in western France where I met two Ukrainian artists whom I'd never met before. It was my first real conversation with Ukrainians since the invasion began, and I felt a sense of dread. They told me right away that they wanted to speak with me in English, rather than Russian, because of the negative associations they have with the Russian language. We ended up having a very good conversation about our work, and I felt grateful to them for speaking with me so openly. In the end, they asked me not to post anything about our encounter on social media because they worried there might be backlash from the Ukrainian art community.

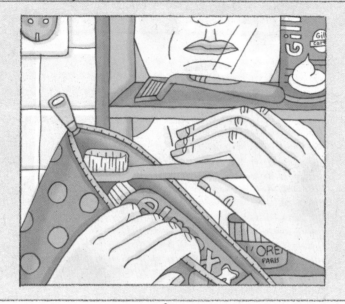

Lately I've been having difficulty breathing. I think it's psychological as I've continued feeling bad emotionally. For the first time in my life, I'm considering seeing a therapist. I'm tired of being in France, and of speaking French. Everyone around me seems to have a normal life, while I don't feel like I belong.

I'm getting lost in this city, and in this country. On a sudden impulse last week, I bought a plane ticket to Istanbul for tomorrow. I also bought a ticket to St. Petersburg from there, and I'll give myself a night in Turkey to decide if I'll go through with this plan.

I haven't told my wife yet. I long for my family so much, and I want to be there for my younger kid's birthday. But I am also worried about getting drafted into the army if I return to Russia.

I read comments by Russians in online chat rooms who said that they had no problems reentering Russia at the border.

I'll decide tomorrow night, once I'm in Istanbul.

Seeing the snow-covered streets of Kyiv, I've been wondering what Copenhagen looks like at the moment, what my kids are doing, and if they are OK. I miss them so much, and I miss the streets of Copenhagen. I'd begun feeling more at home there.

I traveled to the Belarusian border to report. There are concerns that Russia may enter Ukraine once more from the north. I don't think that will happen because the Ukrainian army learned from Russia's first (failed) attempt at invading from the north. I met with many soldiers who told me that everything is going well with the defense in the region so far. The local authorities told me that the territory near the border is swampy and therefore difficult for the Russians and their military vehicles to traverse. When interviewing Ukranians near the Russian border, I have noticed that they seem less afraid of the Russians than people in regions farther away from the border. This seems to be a human instinct: when you are at the center of hell, you can better understand the threat and you learn to deal with it somehow.

After I returned, I took my husband to see a stand-up comedy show in Kyiv. The comedians made jokes about their fear of the bombings, their panic attacks and other aspects of the war.
I really like black humor. I think it's because I'm a journalist, and most of my friends are journalists, too. Cynicism has helped us cope with the horrible things we see, hear and read about.
It protects us from emotional brain damage. Humor is a good cure.

When I arrived in Istanbul on Tuesday, I felt a sense of familiarity. I stayed overnight at my Russian friends' apartment, and they warned me about the danger of returning to Russia. But by the next morning, I had made my decision, and I was on the subway to the airport at 7 AM. The plane to St. Petersburg was almost full, and there were many young men among the passengers. Upon landing, I sent a message to my wife, telling her that I was going to be home for our younger kid's birthday. "Don't get angry," I wrote, "but I'm coming to Russia even if I might get arrested at the border." "Where are you?" she replied, and I responded: "I'm already on my way." No questions were asked at the border, and I entered Russia swiftly.

On the way to my apartment, I stopped to buy flowers, and I found myself on the verge of tears. When I arrived, I rang the downstairs bell and, after being let inside, ran up the stairs to my apartment. I was breathing heavily, and I was nervous. The door opened, and there stood my wife and younger kid (the older one was still at school). I rushed in to hug them, and at that moment, our dog ran towards me and started whining, and didn't stop for another five minutes. I couldn't believe that I was really home and reunited with my family. My wife had been in the middle of preparing a birthday dinner for my child: mashed potatoes, grilled meat, vegetables, red caviar sandwiches and cake. I began to help her right away, and I cooked with great devotion. I had dreamt of cooking with her for so long! I felt immediately that this is where I belong — everything around me is familiar, everything around me is exactly what I love.

Last week, I visited Babyn Yar, the site in Kyiv where Nazi-organized massacres took place during World War II. More than 33,000 Jews died within just a couple of days during one of those massacres. When you walk around the memorial site, you feel a connection to today. It's easy to imagine how millions of people could be eliminated from the face of the earth just because one sick man decides that this is what should happen.

I also thought about the more than 33,000 victims in Turkey and Syria who died during the recent earthquakes. Experts say the number of the dead is still rising. The photos of people trapped in rubble look identical to those from present-day Ukraine. The only difference is that the earthquake wasn't preventable, but this war was. It's hard to find meaning in life amid all this horror. I don't think that this war will end soon. As long as Russia is run by a fascist, the shelling will continue. When people tell me that Russia should be destroyed for this war to end, I remind them of the fact that it'll always be our neighbor. If we retaliate, the war could last for decades. If the Russians lose this war — and I know they will — they could try to attack us, or other countries, again in the future. Destroying Russia won't solve anything. There needs to be space for us to rebuild our relationship.

Before the invasion, my husband and I used to celebrate Valentine's Day. We would just stay at home and enjoy a quiet evening. But this year, we have too much work to celebrate.

I quickly transitioned back into my old St. Petersburg routine: I walk the dog, go shopping and cook meals for the family. It feels as if the past four months of separation never happened. During the first few days, I focused entirely on my wife and children. But then I started watching the news again, and reality returned. How can I make plans for my life when my country is causing all this suffering? Now that we're nearing the war's one-year anniversary, my wife worries that the government will close Russia's borders and institute a new draft. We've decided that I should return to France soon, so I bought a plane ticket for the end of the week. My plan is to explore Marseille as an option next because renting a place there is cheaper than in other parts of France. It feels like I'm on a new mission. Perhaps it'll be easier for me emotionally this time. Today is Valentine's Day. Even though it isn't part of the Russian tradition, we'll go to a restaurant in our neighborhood tonight to celebrate.

One of my friends here told me about the many farewell parties she has been to lately. She herself would like to emigrate, but can't because she is a single mother and doesn't have enough funds. Another friend of mine returned to Russia after having tried to make a new life in the U.S. for a few months. He told me that, for him, Russia is the best place on earth because, despite how messed up it is, his business has been flourishing. If it weren't for the war, I would feel the same way. Everything I need is here: my family, my friends, my work. If the war ends soon, I'd like to return to Russia — and to become a better artist. I want my work to focus more on human values.

The other day, my husband said to me: "Look at us! Just a few months ago, we couldn't imagine wearing colorful clothes. It would have felt sinful. And now we're even going to parties and enjoying ourselves in the middle of this war zone!" Last week, we went to see another comedy show. It helps us not to feel trapped in our dark thoughts about the war and our future. The last year has taught us that war isn't the worst thing that can happen to you. The worst thing is when there aren't any moments of happiness left — when you feel dead inside. I've noticed that I sometimes don't feel anything when scrolling through news feeds about the victims of Russia's attacks, and that scares me. But I know that this sense of emotional numbness will pass. The emptiness and the pain — one day they'll disappear.

At the beginning of the invasion, I had so much hatred in my heart. I loathed everyone who lives in Russia, and even though I knew that not everyone there had done something bad, I was full of hate because Russians weren't doing anything to stop the horror that's been going on for an entire year already. When I realized I had these feelings, I felt disgusted with myself. We grow up being taught not to cause each other harm, to live in peace with those around us, and suddenly, we find ourselves wishing death upon those who have invaded our country. And this wish for death runs very deep. It's scary.
The animosity between Ukrainians and Russians will remain with us for years, decades even. People my age won't be able to let go of those feelings. It's something that we'll leave for our children to resolve. And I'm sure that, somehow, in the future, they will work it out.

I returned to France two nights ago. The day before I left, I had a strange feeling — as if I could no longer remember the reason why I had to leave Russia. My younger kid begged me not to go, and I really didn't want to leave. Now I'm back in France, in a town near the seaside. It's warm and springlike, and it feels like I'm on vacation — and I still don't understand why I'm here. This week, Putin will give a speech on the one-year anniversary of the invasion, and perhaps there will be a new draft. But now I'm wondering if all of this is really reason enough for me to leave my country and my family. I'm afraid of losing touch with them. Perhaps it's just because I lost my emotional connection to my own father a long time ago. I don't want the same thing to happen to my children and me. St. Petersburg is where I belong.

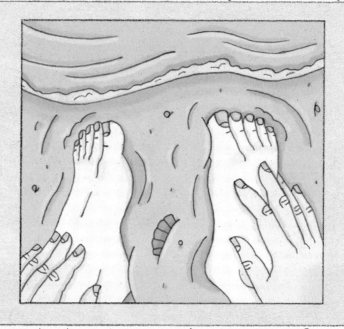

Wars are waged to demonstrate strength and superiority. But in my eyes, all that war demonstrates is stupidity. Clearly, we've learned nothing from all the wars of the past. We should know by now that war is meaningless. This war has made me forget what it feels like to think about the future. I've just been living in the here and now. Thinking about the future scares me because I no longer feel that I have any control over it. The war has taught me how important it is to support the people around you, even if you yourself are feeling bad. I've begun telling my wife and children more often that I love them. Before the war, I rarely used those words.

This war has also shown me that you cannot influence your government in any way. It's terrible, but it's a fact.

Acknowledgments

I feel indebted to Terry Tang, editor of the *Los Angeles Times* editorial page, for her long-lasting commitment to this project; to my editor, Kimmy Tejasindhu, and my art director, Chloe Rawlins, at Ten Speed Press for their guidance; and, most of all, to D. and K. for their time, openness and trust.

I also want to thank the following people:

Beniamino Ambrosi, Elyse Cheney, Adam Eaglin and Isabel Mendia at the Cheney Agency; Elaine Trevorrow at the EMT Agency; Corto Blommaert, Anne van Driel, Toris Heijkant, Koos Jeremiasse, Marije Randewijk, Leo Reijnen and Sophia Twigt at *De Volkskrant*; Stefano Cipolla and Sabina Minardi at *L'Espresso*; Carolin Gasteiger at the *Süddeutsche Zeitung*; Alberto Sotelo Alvarez at *El País*; Marco Ghidelli and Barbara Gizzi at Studio RAUM Italic; Felix Cruz, David Drake, David Hawk, Joey Lozada, Mark McCauslin, Dan Myers, Meggie Ramm, Allison Renzulli, Kate Tyler and Aaron Wehner of Ten Speed Press; Britta Egetemeier and Elisabeth Schmitten of Penguin Random House Verlagsgruppe; Noosha Alai-South, Maria Bedford, Shauna Lacy and Fiona Livesey at Penguin UK; my student assistants, Stella Bellow and Miriam Spalinski; and Kathy Belden, Jim Cooke, Claudia Cucchiarato, Liese Mayer, Mykhailo Dianov, Simone Dollmann, Lorena Jones, Lasse Krug, Franz Krug, Rita Krug, Timothy Snyder, Emine Ziyatdinova, S. and A.

———

To support Ukraine, you can donate to the United24 Fund, the Journalist Support Fund 2402 or UNICEF Ukraine.

Image Sources

Pages 4–5: Geological Map of Europe, Touring Club Italiano
Page 13: Postcard featuring Velyka Volodymirska Street in Kyiv/Ukraine
Page 30: Postcard featuring Prymorsky Boulevard in Odessa/Ukraine
Page 69: Postcard featuring the Women's Night School of Sumy/Ukraine
Page 97: Postcard featuring the harbor of Yalta, Crimea/Ukraine

About the Author

NORA KRUG is the author and illustrator of *Belonging*, a visual memoir about WWII and her German family history, which was named a Best Book of 2018 by the *New York Times*, *The Guardian*, NPR and others, and which was the winner of the National Book Critics Circle Award in 2019. She is the illustrator of the graphic adaptation of *On Tyranny*, by Timothy Snyder, named a *New York Times* Best Graphic Novel of 2021. Her short-form graphic biography, *Kamikaze*, about a surviving Japanese World War II pilot, was included in editions of *Best American Comics* and *Best American Nonrequired Reading*. She is the recipient of fellowships from the Maurice Sendak Foundation, Fulbright, the John Simon Guggenheim Memorial Foundation and the Pollock-Krasner Foundation, and has received gold medals from the Society of Illustrators and the New York Art Directors Club. Krug was named Illustrator of the Year by the Victoria and Albert Museum in 2019. She is an associate professor at Parsons School of Design in New York City.

To S. and A.

PARTICULAR BOOKS

UK | USA | Canada | Ireland | Australia
India | New Zealand | South Africa

Penguin Books is part of the Penguin Random House group of companies
whose addresses can be found at global.penguinrandomhouse.com

Portions of this book were serialized in the *Los Angeles Times* between
February 2022 and February 2023. Excerpts also appeared in *L'Espresso* (Italy),
El País (Spain), *Süddeutsche Zeitung* (Germany) and *De Volkskrant* (Holland).

The authorized representative in the EEA is Penguin Random House Ireland,
Morrison Chambers, 32 Nassau Street, Dublin D02 YH68

A CIP catalogue record for this book is available from the British Library

ISBN: 978-0-241-64202-3

Printed and Bound in Italy by L.E.G.O. s.p.A.

www.greenpenguin.co.uk

MIX
Paper | Supporting
responsible forestry
FSC® C018179
www.fsc.org

Penguin Random House is committed to a
sustainable future for our business, our readers
and our planet. This book is made from Forest
Stewardship Council® certified paper.